THE W
TO LIvE

To Estelle & Abraham.

With our Love & Best Wishes

Many thanks for all your support.

Ray & Caroline

THE WILL TO LIVE

ROY & CAROLINE HAYIM

JANUS PUBLISHING COMPANY
London, England

First published in Great Britain 1995
by Janus Publishing Company
Edinburgh House, 19 Nassau Street
London W1N 7RE

British Library Cataloguing-in-Publication Data
A catalogue record for this book is available
from the British Library.

ISBN 1 85756 154 6

Cover design Linda Wade

Phototypeset by Intype, London
Printed and bound in England by
Antony Rowe Ltd, Chippenham, Wiltshire

CONTENTS

BOTULISM

Botulism is caused by a neurotoxin produced by the bacterium CLOSTRIDIUM BOTULINUM. The name is derived from the word 'botulus' or sausage following the first attribution in Germany to eating sausages. Typically, the bacteria contaminate various types of processed food – notably fish, meat, mushrooms and most recently in the U.K., yoghurt. Home bottling or canning of foods has been particularly associated with the condition. Different types of CLOSTRIDIUM BOTULINUM produce various neurotoxins.

The neurotoxin is extremely potent and rapidly spreads through the blood stream to attach itself to the nerves which activate the muscles of the body. As a result of this attachment, which is irreversible, the nerves are no longer able to make the muscles contract. In addition, the nerves which control the contraction of 'smooth' muscle are affected: this results in paralysis of the pupils, the bowels, the bladder and, to some extent, the blood vessels. Secretions of the salivary and other glands may be affected causing dryness of the mouth. Virtually all the muscles which are under voluntary control normally may be made weak or paralyzed. Thus the eyelids droop, eye movements may be lost, chewing, facial expression, swallowing, speech and breathing are affected: in addition the muscles of the trunk, arms and legs are weakened.

As noted above, the neurotoxin binds irreversibly to the motor nerves: recovery, however, is possible because the nerves may sprout new attachments to their muscles over a period of time. Treatment is firstly to remove the source of the toxin, to give antitoxin which mops up the toxin still circulating in the blood and to maintain the vital functions and nutrition of the patient until the body's own repair processes allow activation of the muscles again.

In the last few years the toxin of CLOSTRIDIUM BOTULI-NUM has found an important medical use in the treatment of abnormal muscular movements. Tiny doses are injected into the abnormally active muscles and effectively reduce their strength of contraction.

Professor C M Wiles
Professor of Neurology
University of Wales College of Medicine

The toxins produced by c. botulinum are among the most poisonous ever discovered – the lethal dose for humans is about one-millionth of a gram.
Life – The Science of Biology
by Purves Orians Heller
Third Edition

PROLOGUE

ROY WOKE up at three o'clock the next morning and was violently sick, only just making it to the bathroom in time. It felt as if he had emptied out the entire contents of his stomach as he gripped onto the edge of the basin for fear of passing out. His skin felt clammy, his vision was blurred.

That should clear it, he reasoned, knowing from old that vomiting usually marked the first stage in the recovery process. It was probably the lunch on the plane that was responsible, although he reckoned that having only eaten a mouthful it shouldn't have had that great an effect.

'Are you all right?'

Caroline stood sleepily in the doorway and gazed down at him in concern.

'Mmm,' he mumbled. 'Must have been that meal on the plane.'

His throat felt dry making it difficult to talk and his words were barely audible. Hating to be made a fuss of, Roy crawled back into bed.

'Shall I call the doctor?' she suggested tentatively, knowing his opinion of the medical profession.

Roy stiffened perceptibly and tried to maintain a semblance of dignity.

'Most certainly not,' he croaked tartly. 'It's only a stomach upset. I should be all right in the morning. No point in dragging the poor man out in the middle of the night for a stomach upset is there?'

Caroline looked at him thoughtfully, taking out her medical dictionary to look up food poisoning. She slipped downstairs to mix the recommended drink of cold milk and water which Roy did his best to swallow. It seemed to help ease the tightness around his chest, which she massaged gently until he fell asleep. Caroline herself slept fitfully, conscious of her husband's uneven breathing beside her and troubled by a vague feeling of unease.

At six o'clock Roy woke up to make another mad dash to the bathroom. Caroline was immediately by his side, sensing that something was very wrong. He was sick again and began to choke on his own vomit, preventing him from breathing properly. Roy was feeling thoroughly bewildered, he had never felt this sensation before. He was fighting for breath.

Caroline helped him back to bed.

'I'm calling the doctor,' she announced firmly and this time there were no objections. Indeed, he felt strangely detached from the whole scene, like a spectator of a bizarre drama. When she came back, the nausea had subsided and he lay exhausted on the bed.

'Dr Page is not on duty but his locum is coming around within the next half-hour,' she announced.

Fortunately the doctor was quicker than expected, as Roy's vision was deteriorating rapidly and his breathing becoming more laboured. The doctor questioned Caroline quietly about Roy's symptoms while he did a brief physical examination.

'Tell me a bit more about the double-vision,' he asked as he tapped lightly on Roy's chest.

Caroline did her best to recall when it had started, remembering guiltily that neither of them had paid much attention to Roy's complaint at the time. The doctor finally turned to her and said decisively, 'Mrs Hayim, I'm going to call an ambulance. I think he ought to be in hospital immediately.'

Roy stiffened in horror, hospital being the last place he wanted to end up. Caroline looked alarmed but was glad that someone else was taking control of what was becoming a frightening situation. She showed the doctor where the phone was and went back to calm Roy.

'I'm not . . . to hospital,' he whispered feebly, sinking back into the pillow with the effort of talking.

'Roy, it's probably only for tests and you'll be out again in a few hours,' she pleaded, hoping that he wouldn't stubbornly refuse to go.

What if I can't breathe in the ambulance, he thought.

'They are the experts: they will know what to do and it's far better that you are in a hospital where you can be looked after.'

Caroline decided not to disturb the girls but went into Alex's room, shaking him softly on the shoulders until he opened his eyes, still groggy with sleep. She didn't want to ring Saul or her mother to get them to come over and felt that at fourteen, Alex was responsible enough to look after the other two for a couple of hours.

'Daddy's not well Alex, so he's going to hospital,' she whispered. 'Don't wake the others but look after them until I get back. I'm going to follow the ambulance in my car.'

At the mention of an ambulance, Alex sat bolt upright and looked frightened.

'It's all right,' she reassured him. 'It's probably only food poisoning but the doctor wants to have him under observation in case it's something worse.'

The ambulance crew arrived and carried Roy down the stairs strapped onto a chair. There was a man and woman but Roy could not see them properly as his vision was very blurred and he was unable to see clearly. They were chatting cheerfully to Roy and Caroline while they lifted him into the back of the ambulance.

'Where are we going,' Roy muttered, holding onto the edge of the chair to steady himself. He looked at Caroline with a slightly glazed expression in his eyes, trying to say something else but unable to form the words.

'We're heading for the Edgware General because the Royal Free is full,' the driver said cheerfully. 'You'll be in good hands there. Do you know the way,' he continued, addressing Caroline.

She nodded and looked at the closing doors of the ambulance with a sinking heart, praying that he would be all right on the journey. She went back into the house to fetch some of Roy's belongings in case he was asked to stay in for a few days and packed them in a small case.

The early morning air had a cold nip to it, although it promised to be a warm day. There was thankfully little traffic and she tore down the Edgware Road towards the hospital. Caroline felt as if she had suddenly been spirited down into a TV hospital drama and had come by mistake into the wrong scene. Somehow she couldn't take in that Roy was ill . . . seriously ill . . . and on the way to hospital. It seemed so unreal that part of her wanted to dismiss it altogether, to turn off the television set and to return to bed as if none of this had really happened at all.

Roy sat in the semi-darkness of the ambulance, unable to see out of the high, narrow window or take in much of the cold grey dawn. The woman sat in the front with the driver and he could hear them chatting quietly between themselves. It was soothing to hear the quiet hum of their voices against the engine but he also felt slightly lonely. There didn't seem to be any traffic at that hour of the morning and they drove swiftly down the main Edgware Road. Thank God there was no siren blaring out but would Caroline know where they were going?'

What if I choke again?

The thought hit him in the face and he jerked his head involuntarily back. Caroline wasn't there to help him and he doubted whether the ambulance crew would realise soon enough to come back to help? For the first time, he sensed an icy spasm of fear darting down his spine and he felt utterly alone. *What if I have another vomiting fit and can't catch my breath*?

He talked himself through the fear until his heart had stopped pounding against his chest, like some sort of prisoner clamouring to get out. The stiffness in his chest eased and his breathing became more regular.

There! Triumphantly he congratulated himself on the back for averting another attack and then sank back into the chair, the effort having cost too much in terms of will power and energy. Suddenly he was beyond caring and his mind drifted pleasantly away into a dream world. He was back in the South of France, swimming in the deep blue sea, his mind floating gently on the waves. Bliss. He drifted away to the soft purr of the engine.

Roy was brought abruptly back to the present as the ambulance came to a standstill and they opened the doors. The lights streamed in, harsh reality intruding on his wandering thoughts and reawakening the old fear.

The driver and his companion appeared and lifted him gently up with the minimum of fuss.

'I can't . . . breathe,' he whispered to the man.

It came out as a desperate whisper, an anguished cry that didn't sound at all like his voice and which gave part of him quite a shock.

'Oh yes you can,' the man boomed out, his face looming down over him. Roy saw the huge finger approach as it crashed down on his chest and shot through him like a red-hot iron. As he entered the hospital, he lost consciousness and the dark peace of oblivion swallowed him up completely.

Chapter One

HOLIDAY

IN MANY ways, forty-nine-year-old Roy Hayim had reached the pinnacle of his life. Born in Bombay of Jewish parents, he had married within the faith four years after setting up his own business, later to become an established surveying and estate agency practice. Theirs was a happy and traditional marriage, where Roy saw himself most firmly as the head of the household while Caroline centered her life around the home and children. All major decisions and financial concerns were left to Roy although Caroline exerted her influence in more subtle ways through the sheer strength of her personality. Indeed they made an excellent team together with their three children. They had many friends and their home in Basing Hill was always a lively one with frequent visitors, in fact they loved company and liked to think that they had an open home.

Not that they hadn't had their share of trouble. Tragedy had already struck once when at nineteen months their youngest child Naomi fell ill with meningitis. As a result she became deaf and wouldn't leave Caroline's side or let her out of her sight during the following year. They decided to employ a series of au pairs to help out for the next few years until the children were older and then breathed a sigh of relief when they felt they no longer needed them. Roy and Caroline began what was to be an ongoing fight to have Naomi attend a normal hearing school. Contrary to professional opinion, they were anxious that she should learn to speak rather than sign so that she would be able to mix easily in the hearing world. They sent her to a hearing playschool and Caroline gave her much extra help at home. Although Noami did spend four years in a particularly good special school until she was nine, she was being transferred that September to a primary school in Maida Vale where she would be prepared for a secondary education in a normal, hearing mainstream school. It was as much a tribute to her parents as any specialist care that she would be able to cope with the competitive curriculum of mainstream education and lead a normal social life.

In 1968, together with his close friend Eric Shapiro, Roy had set up a small residential and professional practice. With little capital but with hard work, they very quickly made an impact in Boreham Wood. The agency steadily flourished, culminating in its amalgamation with the well established practice of a Mr Moss Kaye, who was nearing retirement and lacking an heir. The firm carved a comfortable niche for itself in north-west London and was regarded by most leading companies as experts in that area. Moss Kaye and Roy Frank, as they were now called, gradually sold up their smaller offices and, in 1986, moved closer to the West End, setting up at Swiss Cottage in what was to be their most ambitious expansion. They took on extra staff, their overheads were much larger and both Roy and Eric were under considerable pressure to make ends meet. It was a challenging but exhausting time, particularly for Roy who had a deeply rooted inability to delegate and insisted on overseeing even the tiniest project himself. Despite a blustery temper and a pernickety attention to detail, he won the affection and loyalty of his colleagues and staff turnover was low. Moreover, it looked as if the firm was going to pull through the difficult period and by the time the summer of 1987 came, Roy was able to consider leaving the office for his annual holiday with the family.

It was definitely time for a holiday, Roy thought as he surveyed the usual Sunday morning chaos surrounding him while he attempted to read the newspaper. Caroline was cooking the breakfast amidst the noisy chatter of their three children Alex, Rachel and Naomi. When all parental threats to quieten their fractious squabbles had failed, Caroline came up with some earth-shattering news to silence the arguments.

'Who wants to hear where we're going on holiday this year?' she announced finally, a triumphant gleam in her eyes.

The two girls sat up eagerly. Even fourteen-year-old Alex paid attention and looked at her with interest. Only Roy sat there smouldering at yet another interruption to the Sunday Times.

'Well . . . we thought that we haven't been abroad for a couple of years now and it'd be really nice to go somewhere hot,' Caroline continued, keeping them in suspense a bit longer. 'So, we decided that . . .'

She had them all now, waiting impatiently for her to go on.

'. . . maybe the South of France would be a good idea.'

Alex's eyes lit up as he envisaged days of swimming in the clear blue Mediterranean Sea, trips on boats and scuba-diving amongst exotic fish and coral reefs.

'I could take my snorkling gear,' he cried, an avid enthusiast of the murky life under the seas.

'We'd have to fly, wouldn't we,' Naomi chipped in, her face shining with excitement at the thought of such an adventure, while Rachel grinned cheerfully, the gloom of the impending summer examinations fading rapidly. Part of her was already racing along an endless sandy beach, or persuading her father to take them out in a boat.

Roy looked at their excited faces and grinned, his earlier irritation melting as quickly as it came.

'Now it's not definite, but your mother and I have given it some serious thought,' he explained. 'We thought we might stay in a hotel, but we found that the ones we liked were exorbitantly expensive, so we've opted for a self-catering holiday instead.'

Caroline rushed to get the brochure and enthusiastically showed it to the children.

'I've been looking at ads in the Sunday Times and I think this one is definitely the best value,' she said. 'It's a modern apartment block between Antibes and Nice with our own cooking facilities, swimming pool, tennis courts . . .'

They all poured over the pictures in the glossy brochure and gave the apartments and the swimming pool full marks of approval, having waved aside any possible objections.

'Much better to be independent,' Roy agreed with his wife. 'That way we can be our own masters, eat exactly when we want to and not rely on the rigid hotel meal times.'

'Just think,' said Roy, 'all those mouth-watering fruits and vegetables, fresh fish minutes out of the sea, just waiting for us in the market! This time we can pick and choose what we want and bring it home to cook. Or have picnics on the beach perhaps? No more being tied to a hotel timetable.'

These domestic details were of little interest to the children who were already making plans to bring tennis rackets, skateboards and a vast array of games for the beach. Caroline left them in peace, knowing that she would have to exercise a firm veto when it came to packing but was enjoying their high spirits for the moment.

'It's not much more expensive to take a larger flat,' Roy observed, flicking through the brochure again.

Thoughtfully, Caroline looked over his shoulder at the price list.

'You're right, there's not much to choose between them. It would be nice to have loads of space, what with the children's clutter all over the place. We could even invite friends to join us . . . or better still, why don't we ask Mum to come for a week or so. She hasn't been on a real holiday for ages, not since Dad died.'

'Good idea,' Roy remarked drily. 'Why don't we invite the rest of your family!'

'Why not indeed!' she said, ignoring the faint note of sarcasm that had crept into his voice. 'After all, Saul and Emilie could do with a break this year. It would be fun to have the whole family together for a while – perhaps for a week or so in the middle of our three weeks?' she said hopefully.

Roy sighed, resigning himself to an invasion from his in-laws. Not that he really minded as he got on well with them all, and enjoyed the long heated discussions with Saul he always seemed to end up having after dinner. But he feared that agreeing too readily would add fuel to Caroline's enthusiastic generosity and before he knew it half of the neighbourhood would be accompanying them to the South of France.

'I have a cousin with an apartment in Nice,' he added, not to be outdone on the family front, 'we could meet up with her too.'

Caroline smiled and made no further comment, longing to be able to ring her mother to break the good news but deciding to let Roy get used to the idea for a little while. Indeed, he had no choice, for the holiday was their main topic of conversation over the following weeks. It was mid-June and because they were booking rather late, the choice of available apartments was somewhat limited. None the less, they managed to get more or less exactly what they wanted and organised to have Caroline's family join them for ten days in the middle. They always went away for the last three weeks of August, arriving home on the Bank Holiday weekend so that Roy had a day to recover before going back to work. Moreover,

August was generally a quiet month for the property market and so he felt that he could leave his department in the competent hands of his junior partner, Graham.

As the day neared, Roy began his usual frantic attempt to put his office affairs in order.

'We're only going for three weeks, Roy,' Caroline remarked calmly. 'Surely some of those appointments could wait until you come back.'

'Nothing can wait in my line of work,' he grumbled. 'If you don't seize the opportunity now, you'll have missed your chance. I don't know why I bother to go on holiday at all, I'm so exhausted from getting things organised at the office that I sometimes wonder if it's worth the effort.'

'You just haven't learned to delegate,' she replied briskly, ignoring his grumpy humour. It was always the same the week before they went away. Suddenly everything just had to be done that week and a month's worth of appointments were squeezed into those last few days. 'You're not the only one who can do the work, y'know. Graham's perfectly capable of holding the fort without you, and if he needs advice he can always ask Eric. He is a senior partner, in case you have forgotten!'

'But, I'm in charge of the agency side,' Roy protested with his usual bluster. 'Eric has enough on his plate and I'm the only one who seems to do things properly in my department.'

'Oh rubbish,' she exploded in exasperation. 'You've a perfectly good team in there, and you're always saying how reliable Graham is . . . and loyal too. I'd have left months ago if I worked for you, what with your grouchy humour and complete lack of confidence in anyone else.'

Roy didn't argue, suspecting that she was right. He had trained the junior partner himself and knew him to be sound. And yet, somehow he couldn't rest easy until he had double and triple checked everything. He smiled self-consciously, able to laugh at himself while feeling at the same time a slight annoyance. What did she know of business affairs?

'You probably even insist on sticking the stamps onto the letters and posting them yourself.' Caroline continued ruthlessly. 'It beats me how they can stand it.'

But stand it they did, and for all his tight control and fastidious insistence on perfection, Roy commanded the respect and affection of his colleagues, and the staff turnover at Moss Kaye and Roy Frank was strikingly low.

'Look, I'll finish up by midday on Friday,' Roy announced firmly, changing the subject which was becoming too uncomfortable for his liking. 'That'll give me time to do my packing and get any last-minute things at the shops that we might need.'

Caroline glanced at him in amazement. Roy always left his packing to the eleventh hour and barely managed to get himself organised, let alone help her deal with the mountains of clothes, towels and games that had to be squeezed into three rather delapidated-looking suitcases. With a smile, she left him to his own devices as he searched for his favourite pair of swimming trunks, given to him by her father ten years ago and already a collector's item . . .

Once Roy finally disengaged himself from the office and pronounced himself to be 'on holiday' the mood of excitement escalated tenfold. The children restlessly awaited his return, knowing from old that he would shed the office, layer by layer, on the drive home and be full of fun and good humour when he walked through the door. Whilst Caroline was busy organising the neighbours to keep an eye on the house, Roy was able to add fuel to the children's wildest fantasies and plan a mind-boggling array of adventures and outings. Whether any of these would actually materialise was beside the point; what the three youngsters wanted at that moment was to indulge in imaginative flights of fancy, so that by the time evening fell they were too excited to sleep or even finish their dinner.

'I'll help you,' offered Alex, and Roy dubiously agreed to let him watch so long as he didn't disturb his concentration.

Roy's wardrobe was the last legacy from his army days, and each item was divided into separate compartments. Nothing caused him more irritation than to find an odd sock, and the whole house would suffer until its partner had been found.

Packing took a similar regimented path, starting with socks and shoes and working upwards systematically to the head. Vests, handkerchiefs, pyjamas . . . all had their set order in the suitcase. Alex knew this off by heart and loved the ritual of the process, particularly if he knew he was allowed to lay them out in the suitcase in neat folds. Roy's hopes that Alex might learn some of his discipline had long since evaporated, since his bedroom usually looked as though a bomb had hit it. His powers of organisation more closely resembled a tube station, with everyone flying around in seeming chaos and yet managing to get to the right place only as if by some lucky chance.

By the time Sunday morning arrived, Caroline was already exhausted. Checking that the heating was switched off, sending the children swarming all over the house to pull out the plugs, double locking the doors and windows, remembering cameras, passports, tickets . . . Roy was up at six o'clock to set the ball rolling but even still, they were only just ready by the time the taxi arrived. She was too tired to even give much thought to the flight, a fact for which she was grateful as she had developed a deep fear of flying ever since her brother had been killed in an airplane crash years earlier. If she had insisted, they could have gone overland but she knew that it would waste precious days of their holiday and undo any good that the holiday might do with the strain of travelling.

At the airport, Roy shepherded his offspring to the boarding gates, checking them all in on the way and stopping briefly in the duty-free shop.

'I'll get a bottle of sherry for your mother and some whisky in case we have any visitors,' he told Caroline, who was attempting to ration the number of sweets and comics per child.

'You've almost another suitcase full there, Rachel,' he scolded her half-heartedly, unwilling to dampen her excitement as she chose two crossword puzzle books and a pile of sweets. She laughed and ignored him, stubbornly clutching her spoils. Of all the children, she was the most like her father and consequently clashed most frequently with his fiery temper. Watching the determined toss of her head, Roy grinned ruefully, recognising the gesture as his own and seeing in his twelve year old many of his own choleric tendencies. Naomi at nine was outwardly far more compliant, and yet could twist most of them around her little finger with her sunny nature.

'Bags the window seat,' Naomi cried, and Rachel immediately objected that it wasn't fair.

'Alex always get a window because he always sits beside Daddy,' she complained. 'Naomi can't have it for the whole way.'

'Shh, you two . . .' Caroline remonstrated. 'You can take it in turns and I'll sit by the aisle. Now pick up all your bits and pieces, we're about to board.'

Amidst further wranglings they trooped onto the plane, Roy breathing a mixture of relief and surprise that they had survived the first part of the journey and Caroline a sigh of apprehension. Naomi disappeared momentarily, only to be discovered up front with the cabin crew tucking into a glass of orange juice, courtesy of the airline.

'How does that child always manage to get all the freebies going?' Roy smiled in wonder, while her siblings promptly sent her back to get more for them.

'Maybe people feel sorry for her because they realise she is deaf,' Caroline mused, pushing all of their hand luggage into the overhead compartment, praying that it wouldn't reappear on top of some unsuspecting passenger's head, so hard was it to shut the door.

'Maybe . . . but she is well able to make herself understood for all that,' Roy said affectionately. 'She's as capable as the other two, even though she's only nine,' and they both laughed as the three children returned to their seats, laden down with more gifts.

'Right, sit down and fasten your seat belts now,' demanded Caroline. 'You take the window for the first half of the journey Naomi, and swap with Rachel for the second half.'

Rachel opened her mouth to object but was pre-empted by her father, sitting beside her: 'And I'll be the judge of half way.'

Caroline only really relaxed as the plane landed in Nice Airport. The flight had been reasonably calm and she had buried herself in a book to take her mind off the queasy feeling in her stomach. Roy and the children had tucked into the special kosher meal which they ordered as they thought it would make a change from the vegetarian meal that was on offer. In fact it had been a simple but splendid meal, living up to all of Roy's hungry expectations. As a result he booked a similar meal for the return flight, so impressed had he been with the quality of the food. The meat was tender, the salad crisp, warm bread to mop up the juices and dressings and all washed down by a very acceptable wine.

'First fresh meal I've ever had on a plane,' he remarked cheerfully. 'I can't remember aircraft food ever tasting so good,' and he disappeared to collect the luggage, leaving Alex behind to guard the trolley. No sooner was he back when he went off again, this time to collect the car keys from the rental company.

'Far better to be independent,' he had insisted, when Caroline had queried the expense of renting a car for the whole three weeks.

'We can go wherever we want rather than rely on those local buses and should be able to see a good bit of the countryside.'

'I want to go to the beach,' Rachel put in, sensing that her mother's notions of sightseeing might not be to her taste.

'We can go to all the beaches you want,' he smiled benevolently, 'but there is no point in staying in one place for too long.'

'No danger of *you* ever doing that,' Caroline retorted, knowing that Roy's tolerance level for lying on hot beaches was minimal.

Rachel frowned.

'Daddy, I hope we are not going to spend the whole holiday in this car now that you have rented it,' she said sternly, and both parents burst out laughing.

'You pick up that bag over there and be quiet,' Roy commanded, watching his daughter scurry off to retrieve her rucksack which was in danger of falling off the trolley.

By the time they had battled their way through the crazy Riviera traffic and had got lost on a couple of occasions, even Roy was in need of a swim. The minute they got to the apartment they abandoned their cases and found the pool, wallowing in its warm water and the soft heat of the early evening sun. Roy and Caroline returned to survey their new temporary home and to start the marathon task of unpacking. Roy sank back into the deep chairs and looked out with satisfaction over the balcony onto the rooftops of the town below. They sparkled in the sunshine and reflected the shimmering light of the sea beyond.

'Perfect! Just think, no office for three whole weeks,' he gloated. 'No phone calls, no nagging clients . . . perfect bliss. Now, I think a stiff whisky is in order. What will you have?'

Caroline opted for a glass of sherry and went back inside, leaving him to his thoughts as he settled himself on the balcony with his drink, and let the soft, balmy air envelop him.

Yes, he definitely felt a sense of well-being envelop him, even though the holiday had scarcely begun. Work had become a strain recently and he no longer unreservedly enjoyed going into the office as he had before. Perhaps he was getting old, although at forty-nine, he was hardly approaching the age of retirement.

'A penny for them!'

He was so far away that he hadn't heard Caroline coming up behind him and turned towards her, his face serious.

'Just thinking how much I needed this break. I wonder if I've become stale and tired of the business,' he said anxiously. 'I no longer look forward to going in; there are so many tedious bits of paperwork and administration to be done that it has lost the excitement of the early days.'

'Can't you get someone else to do those routine things!' she suggested helpfully, knowing that he wouldn't take advice she offered about the office seriously.

When it came to decisions about the children or the house, Roy always listened to her attentively and often acted on her advice, but here her domain ended. In many ways, theirs was a traditional marriage, and Roy's Sephardi background meant that he assumed the definite patriarchal role of head of the household.

The doorbell rang and Caroline went to open it, discovering the cleaning lady on the threshold with milk and fresh bread. Although voluble, she didn't speak a word of English but Caroline's knowledge of French was sufficient to make herself understood and she thanked her for her kind thought. Caroline was gratified to learn that she cleaned the flat daily and made the beds, although she later discovered that this was done in a somewhat haphazard way. Still, it liberated her from any real housework for three blissful weeks and she joined Roy on the balcony again, both of them basking in the idea of the much coveted period of leisure that stretched before them.

That August, the entire French Riviera simmered in a heat wave. The mornings started hot and, by midday, the temperature had risen to unbearable heights, drawing all but the most ardent sun-worshippers indoors for a siesta, dropping lethargically upon a bed or under a shady tree. The streets were empty, the shops closed.

Roy paced the room, increasingly frustrated. It was the fourth day of their holiday and he resented the enforced period of rest. Deciding that the blistering heat was the lesser of two evils, he put on a hat to shade his head and went out. Down on the crowded beach it was a different story. Like Roy, the other tourists did not want to know about siestas, regarding sleep as wasting precious time of their costly holiday. Instead, they sat around in cafés along the promenade and drank endless glasses of iced coffee or *citron presse*. The beach was littered with parasols and half-naked bronzed oiled bodies while the marina was packed with boats of every description, rocking gently in the oily water.

Roy shouldered his way through the throngs of milling tourists, the heat becoming oppressive, the day more humid and the air heavy with petrol fumes from the passing cars. Irritation overwhelmed him at the sight of so many people; it was worse than London during the rush-hour. Some had to be French, but the general impression was of a cosmopolitan influx of visitors. Great blond Scandinavian students with hefty rucksacks, Italians and Spaniards gesticulating furiously amongst themselves, and the unmistakable Americans, their checked shirts and trousers brazenly shouting out their nationality for all to hear.

As if suddenly coming to a decision, Roy stopped in mid-stream, ignoring the angry looks from two women who crashed into him and jostled impatiently to get past. That's it! He'd organise a day's outing somewhere. Perfect to get out of this claustrophobic atmosphere. He turned, retracing his steps back to the apartment at twice the speed, the prospect of a day in the cool mountains added fuel to his enthusiasm. He'd plan the trip right now with Caroline, and they could set off early tomorrow.

Climbing the flights of stairs to their apartment, two at a time, he burst into the living room.

'Caroline!'

There was no reply.

'Caroline? Alex?'

Silence. He then spied the hastily written note lying on the table: GONE TO THE BEACH OPPOSITE THE CAFE WE WERE IN YESTERDAY. SEE YOU THERE!

Roy gazed around the empty apartment, disappointed and angry that they weren't there to listen to his great idea. It was only after several cold drinks that he pulled himself together and took out the tourist guidebook to plan the trip for the next day.

Day eight. It was too hot to go on lying on the rumpled bed and Roy couldn't understand Caroline's delight in sleeping in. He jumped out of bed, anxious to greet the early morning heat before it got too strong. Indeed, mornings were the best part of the day, and he usually got up at seven o'clock for a swim before the sun rose in full force.

He collected his swimming trunks and let himself quietly out of the apartment, going down the stairs that led to the swimming pool. Time enough to go back for Alex for their early trip to the market before the others awoke. But first a swim . . .

He dived. It was cool, but already not cool enough for real refreshment. He swam a few lengths and thought with pleasure of the day ahead, his powerful strokes cutting through the water with the calm strength of one who is master of his environment and completely at home in the water. One final length and then he climbed up the steps, reaching for his towel to dry himself. The paving stones felt warm beneath his feet and his skin tingled as the drops of water dried naturally in the morning sun.

Roy changed back into his shorts and gazed down at his tanned legs. They were strong and muscular and he prided himself on being fit and sporty. With a sense of contentment, he returned to the apartment to fetch Alex who enjoyed the trips to the nearby market for croissants or crusty baguettes, wonderfully exotic fruit and freshly ground coffee. Caroline revelled in being able to wake up to the smell of coffee wafting through the rooms, and take a leisurely shower while Roy organised breakfast for everyone and umpired endless discussions about where and how they would spend the day. Today would be different, as he had worked out a detailed itinerary which would take up the whole day. He hadn't told them yet and planned it as a big surprise after breakfast.

They bought extra food for a picnic and returned just as the others were getting up. After breakfast, Roy cleared his throat.

'How about a surprise outing?'

Rachel looked at him suspiciously, torn between her curiosity to know what he had in mind and her desire to go to the beach.

'Where?'

'Wait and see,' he said, teasing her.

'I want to go to the beach.'

'We can't go to the beach every day,' Roy protested peevishly.

'We don't,' she protested stubbornly. 'We've already been to those perfume factories at Grasse and that village up the mountains where that famous artist came from, what was his name . . .?'

Caroline stepped in, sensing that a row was brewing. She understood Rachel's reservations and even Caroline was amazed at what seemed to be Roy's endless source of energy. Trips to vineyards, local ruins, mountain drives . . . he had planned a heavy sightseeing itinerary for them. Not that she minded, as she herself no longer wanted to spend whole days on the crowded French beaches, but she knew that the children were anxious to go swimming as much as possible. So far it had ended with a compromise, so that they

spent the morning at the beach and the afternoon on one of Roy's
expeditions. This suited Caroline to the ground, and even the
children enjoyed Roy's roaming instinct, although they always
grumbled at the moment of leaving the beach so as to make their
protests known. However, today she sensed that this trip was important to Roy and so coaxed the children to give in graciously.

'But where are we going?' Alex demanded.

'Monte Carlo!' Roy announced with a flourish.

All further objections were silenced, for the children had all heard
about Monte Carlo and were anxious to see it for themselves. One
quick dip in the pool and they were ready, and Roy loaded up the
car with a massive picnic which they had all prepared with great
haste and excitement.

They decided to go via the Grande Corniche with spectacular
views overlooking Villefranche and Cap Ferrat passing the charming
village of Eze perched on a hill just below them. A certain jaded
air pervaded the atmosphere, the result of a long summer of harsh
sunshine which left the ground burnt and dry. He had chosen that
particular route as the most scenic and they were not disappointed.
As they climbed up into the mountains, the view became breathtaking, causing the children to lean excitedly out of the windows
for a better look. Frightening hairpin bends, sheer drops falling into
a sunlit yet forbidden sea, grey mountains towering above . . . it was
like driving through another world, and the tiny villages peppered
throughout the countryside had that timeless quality that comes
from being unspoilt by modern life.

Roy drove carefully, apprehensive of the winding roads yet confident enough as a driver to negotiate the most tortuous of bends.
He changed down as they approached a dip in the road and ground
to a halt as the car swung at right angles to the bay.

With one accord they gazed in silence at the view.

Monte Carlo.

It needed no introduction; it lay nestled between two promon-
tories, literally carved into the side of the mountain. They climbed
out of the car and Roy and Caroline savoured the scene, while the
children tottered near the edge of the precipice with alarming
recklessness.

'Naomi, you'll fall,' Caroline said sharply, ushering them back
into the car.

They began the descent to the city and, as they entered, were struck immediately by the contrast to the surrounding countryside. From the rustic, unsophisticated air of the natives in the nearby villages, the populace of Monte Carlo was a mixed lot. Fashionably dressed women in the latest *haute couture* and tanned students in shorts and T-shirts alike strolled through the immaculately clean streets, hosed down every day and adorned with beautiful displays of flowers.

Roy and Caroline were instinctively drawn to the old town, its small cobbled streets opening like labyrinths into little courtyards and flanked by the pink stones of the buildings. They paused to enter the cathedral where Princess Grace was buried before meandering through the winding streets where Caroline stopped in every antique shop along the way.

'For crying out loud, Caroline,' Roy protested in exasperation. 'They're all the same, you know. What on earth do you want to go in *that* one for; it's not as though we have got the money to buy anything there.'

'I just want to look around and see,' she insisted placidly, and he gave in, muttering to himself but knowing that there was little he could do in any case. Fortunately, the children were equally bored and he eventually guided her firmly down to the new part of town, a startling contrast of high-rise apartment blocks and shopping complexes.

For all its modern brash air, the new part had more appeal for the children, and Alex poured over models of marine mammals in the Oceanographic Museum with as much fervour as his mother had over the antique shops. Roy groaned. He hated lingering in one spot, however interesting, and desperately coaxed his eldest child with promises of a visit to the famous casino.

Promises that, alas, could not be fulfilled as they discovered an age limit of over-eighteen. Caroline saved a crisis by offering to buy them all ice-cream at one of the smart open-air cafés.

Whilst the children were munching happily amongst themselves, Caroline and Roy left them to explore the casino and were surprised to discover that it had a ballroom and a theatre as well as the gaming rooms. It stood in well tended and colourful gardens and they paused briefly to enjoy the opulence and sophistication, qualities that pervaded the whole city and which they appreciated the more after the crowded tourist resorts of the past few days.

On their return, and to please the girls, they decided to return to the old quarters to see the changing of the guards at the Pink Palace.

Even Roy didn't tire of Monte Carlo until well after five o'clock and they drove slowly back along the coast. They planned to eat-in for a change as they had a busy day ahead of them, with the arrival of Caroline's mother, her brother Saul, his wife Emilie and their baby David the next morning to swell out the ranks.

They all went to meet them at the airport, waiting impatiently in the arrivals lounge for the plane to land. When Florence, Caroline's mother, walked through customs, Roy rushed forward to help her with her cases genuinely glad to see her. Saul appeared next, carrying a bawling child and looking extremely harassed.

'Roy, good to see you,' he said, shaking his hand and trying to soothe his son. 'Look, there's been a ridiculous mistake and Emilie's been detained by the French police.'

'*What!*'

Roy and Florence gazed at Saul in astonishment, their minds filled with unimaginable horrors.

'They say she's a spy because of her Iranian passport,' he continued. 'They've just stopped her now and won't let her come through. I mean, how absurd can you get!'

Exasperated by the turn of events, Roy disappeared off in the midst of a group of somewhat hostile-looking officials and returned triumphant, bringing a frightened and bewildered Emilie back in tow. Before anyone could be rearrested, particularly that screaming child who was without doubt a disturbance of the peace, Roy bundled them all into the car and drove them back to the flat.

The arrival of Caroline's family did nothing to temper Roy's hectic pace and they toured more and more of the neighbouring countryside by day, and ate out at interesting restaurants by night. It was just too short, and as the three weeks began to draw to a close, Roy felt the old familiar knot in his stomach. He didn't feel ready to go back and would have enjoyed just one more week of the glorious sunshine. The thought of battling with the heavy traffic as he struggled to get to work, and the non-stop phone calls, almost made him groan aloud. Still, he certainly felt more refreshed than before and resolved to banish all niggling thoughts from consciousness until the last minute. When he had to face that telephone again, he would. In the meantime where were the children . . .?

The family had had a week on their own after Saul *et al* returned to London and now it was their turn to go. Amidst protests from the children, Roy and Caroline picked up their belongings and got into the hired car and made the journey to Nice Airport. Somewhat subdued, they boarded the plane without incident and Caroline settled back in her seat uneasily as always, flicking through the duty-free magazine more to distract herself than out of interest. Alex, Rachel and Naomi were gazing through the window drinking in their last views of France as if trying to etch them permanently in their memories.

Roy was looking tanned and refreshed, and although she knew that he was edgy at the prospect of returning to the office, she hoped that the holiday would give him extra energy to deal with it. The stewardess started to wheel the trolley down the aisle.

'That'll be our lunch,' Roy announced, noting the special labels on some of the trays. 'I've ordered the kosher meal again, let's hope it lives up to the one on the journey out.'

'A special kosher meal?' said the Frenchman sitting beside Roy, looking at the approaching trolley with interest.

'Yes,' Roy laughed. 'There's service for you. It was excellent on the flight coming out.'

'Ah, so you probably won't get the usual airline plastic,' his neighbour continued with a smile. 'Maybe I'll order one next time I fly.'

Caroline wasn't particularly hungry but she knew that Roy and the children were. Perhaps a cup of tea would help settle her stomach and at least the meal would take her mind off flying. The meal was sealed in a foil container, but once the top was peeled back the air was filled with an awful smell. Their French friend wrinkled up his nose in disgust.

'Mmm, if that's kosher food, I'll stick with the plastic.'

Caroline looked at the trays anxiously. As Roy and Alex were sitting behind her they had been served first.

'They do smell odd,' she agreed, and tried to open one of the sealed boxes. It was stiff and hard to lift the lid.

'I can't open mine, mummy,' Naomi cried. 'Can you do it for me?'

Caroline leant over and used a thin key supplied to open the lid. As it sprang open, the smell hit her in the face with a force that made her gag.

Naomi was just about to put a forkful of rice in her mouth. 'Don't eat it darling, it smells awful.'

Caroline opened her own box and smelt it.

'Don't touch a thing,' she told the girls in alarm. 'It will make you ill.'

'I'm hungry,' Rachel complained.

'I don't care,' Caroline insisted firmly. 'You can't eat that; it smells terrible. Here, I've some fruit in my bag which will have to do until we get home.'

She looked behind her and saw Alex and Roy tucking into their lunches.

'Don't eat it! How can you eat it, it's foul!'

The note of panic in her voice made Alex put down his fork quickly.

'It does smell a bit funny,' Roy agreed, trying a few mouthfuls of rice and peas before also abandoning the attempt.

'I'd complain to the Chief Rabbi about this if I were you,' the Frenchman said solemnly, a twinkle in his eyes.

Roy gave a shout of laughter.

'I don't suppose many people order kosher meals so goodness knows how long these have been sitting around.'

'How do you manage if you have to eat out, if you don't mind me asking, don't you find it terribly restricting?'

'Not really,' Roy replied, glad of someone to take his mind off his growling stomach. He'd been looking forward to his lunch from the time they arrived at the airport in Nice and was extremely disappointed with the sorry offerings that had been served up. 'We tend to eat fish or the vegetarian menu if we're eating out and there's no kosher food available.'

'Roy, get the stewardess to remove these trays will you please,' Caroline interrupted, beginning to feel slightly nauseous.

Roy caught the stewardess's eye and beckoned her over. She headed in their direction but got waylaid by a passenger on the way.

'I mean, our children go to ordinary schools and we have good friends who are not Jews,' Roy continued, addressing the French-man. 'But where possible, we still try to maintain our customs and laws, and one of those is obviously the special diet.'

Caroline called the stewardess.

Mademoiselle, s'il vous plaît.

She came promptly and Roy showed her the trays.

'Could you remove them please, we're being asphyxiated by the smell,' Caroline asked.

The girl took them up to the front of the cabin at once, apologising profusely and promising to complain to the catering company.

'So much for that,' Roy observed acidly. 'You'd think they could offer us another meal.'

'I've lost my appetite after that smell,' Caroline muttered. 'Let's wait until we get home; I'm sure Saul will have left us bread and milk in the fridge. I don't know how you could even have considered eating it, Roy.'

'Oh you know me,' he grinned cheerfully. 'I've got a cast-iron stomach; I'd eat just about anything.'

The stewardess reappeared to offer them drinks, compliments of the airline, which helped to appease them somewhat and the rest of the journey passed uneventfully. The flight had been short but Roy felt suddenly tired and weak. Drained by the hectic pace of the last few days, filled to the brim with outings, long afternoon walks along the beach, too many late nights and rich dinners, no doubt.

Once the lunch had been cleared, Roy sipped his complimentary drink quietly, cradling it in his hand so as to make it last. He wondered again why he was not feeling more refreshed.

As they approached London and circled above waiting for permission to land, Roy marvelled at the strange beauty of the city. Tall buildings thrusting upwards into the clear blue sky, it's streets winding and twisting, a criss-cross of interlocking roadways forming a grid for miles. Here was a city that offered, in its cosmopolitan urban manner, every conceivable form of culture and entertainment. Crowded, often dirty . . . but it was still home and Roy was pleased to be back.

'Alex, you can get the cases,' he mumbled as they were waiting for their belongings to appear on the conveyor-belt. 'Must be tired after the journey,' he continued.

They arrived home at 2.30 pm and opened up the house.

'Saul's obviously been here,' Caroline remarked with satisfaction as she looked in the fridge. 'Look, he's left some smoked salmon, fresh French sticks and some nice looking cheese. How's that for service?'

The children greedily grabbed hunks of bread and cheese and rushed out into the garden to avoid being enlisted into any of the usual unpacking and household chores. Roy carried the cases upstairs and started to unlock the windows and doors, cheered considerably by the spread that Caroline's brother had laid on. Indeed, they all ate heartily that evening, their appetites whetted by the enforced fast at lunchtime and Caroline looked around her in contentment.

'It's nice to be home, I must admit,' she smiled. 'I mean, I thoroughly enjoyed the whole holiday but it's also lovely being home; you really appreciate it after you've been away.'

Roy grunted dubiously, wondering if he would feel such glowing enthusiasm when he walked into the office on Tuesday.

'I'll clear up,' Caroline offered. 'I want to sort out the laundry while I'm at it.'

Roy didn't insist on helping her but she did notice that he was looking tired again. He wandered into the living room with the children and switched on the television, looking up the paper for the next news. Nine o'clock. Settling back on the sofa he half dozed, feeling suddenly exhausted and a bit weak. Barely able to concentrate on the advertisements, he closed his eyes for a quick nap, opening them only when the news finally came on, and sitting up to keep himself awake.

He couldn't see properly. It felt almost peculiar but everything was double and he rubbed his eyes in disbelief.

'How odd,' he muttered, and Rachel looked up. 'I'm seeing double.'

His speech sounded strange. He was aware of arranging his tongue and lips in the correct position to make the appropriate sound but somehow falling short of the mark. Almost as if he was drunk.

'Why don't you go to bed, Dad,' Alex suggested, hoping to be able to watch a film instead that had just started on another channel.

'I suppose so,' Roy agreed but made no effort to move. 'I really don't feel well at all.'

'Alex is right,' Caroline called from the kitchen having caught the tail end of the conversation. 'Maybe you've caught a bug. Go to bed now and you'll sleep it off; you'll be fine in the morning, you usually are with these sort of things.'

Suddenly Roy made a mad dash for the bathroom and they could hear him being violently sick. He returned, ashen-faced, determined to watch the end of the news at the very least. It was only then that he let himself be persuaded to go to bed and rose to go upstairs.

It was sheer luck that he managed to keep his balance and not fall flat on his face as he manfully tackled the stairs. When Caroline went to check on him twenty minutes later, he was sound asleep and she quietly closed the door. He should be fine in the morning, she thought, and went downstairs to chase the girls up to bed, film or no film.

Chapter Two

EDGWARE GENERAL HOSPITAL

ROY WAS being carried into casualty just as Caroline drove through the gates of the Edgware General Hospital. It took tremendous self-control not to abandon the car in the driveway and rush in after him. Teeth gritted, she parked nearby and hurried back to the casualty department, wanting to be near him as promised so that he wouldn't feel abandoned and alone.

Caroline walked through the doors and resolutely marched up to the woman in the reception area. The receptionist didn't even look up and Caroline's resolve faded as quickly as it had arisen.

'My husband . . . he's just been brought in. Is he all right?' she asked tentatively, her voice sounding hollow and barely audible. She cleared her throat and tried again.

'Excuse me, my name is Caroline Hayim. My husband has just been brought in by ambulance; do you know where he is?'

The receptionist gazed at her blandly, seemingly unaware of the turmoil that was raging within her, a middle-aged woman with the bored air of one who had seen it all and found none of it particularly interesting, she had an impersonal yet not unpleasant look etched firmly on her face.

'Mr Hayim, let's see,' she said, glancing down the admissions list. 'Yes, he's just been brought in and I have his admissions form here. Could I get some particulars from you?'

Caroline shifted impatiently from one foot to the other. Roy had been rushed off to hospital and was God only knows where at the moment, and this woman wanted particulars! As if sensing for the first time Caroline's distress, the receptionist changed tack, her voice suddenly became deliberately gentle and soothing as she explained the procedure.

'One of our registrars is seeing him at the moment and will talk to you afterwards,' she said kindly. 'If you wait here, someone will come to you as quickly as possible. In the meantime, it would really help if we could have a full medical history.'

Caroline calmed down immediately and tried to answer the questions as best as she could, but found her mind in a haze and unable to remember even the most basic things. As if used to dealing with relatives in a state of shock, the receptionist patiently jogged her memory, repeating the questions and doing her utmost to get consistent information.

'Thank you very much,' she said finally as they reached the last item and Caroline gratefully escaped to the seclusion of the waiting area. There was no one else there and she sat on the farthest seat against the wall, glad of the opportunity to gather her thoughts together.

Her peace was short-lived. There was suddenly a terrible commotion in a nearby cubicle as doctors in white coats came running from all sides.

'He's having trouble breathing,' she heard someone shout, and there was a clanging of oxygen cylinders.

Caroline gazed with sympathetic detachment. Thank God Roy only had food poisoning; she pitied the relatives of that poor man. She listened tensely until the fuss died down.

'He seems to be reasonably stable now,' a male voice said, emerging from behind the screen, and she saw now that it belonged to the young, dark-haired doctor who had rushed past her recently. 'Monitor him closely on the ventilator and call me if there's any change. I'll organise for him to be moved to Intensive Care.'

Shortly afterwards, the casualty sister approached Caroline.

'Mrs Hayim? Could you come with me, this way please?'

She led Caroline into a small side room off the main waiting area.

'We'll have more privacy here,' she explained, gesturing towards the chair.

Caroline sat down heavily on the chair and hoped that the sister wouldn't notice that she was shaking.

'I'm terribly sorry, but I'm afraid that your husband has taken a turn for the worse. He's stopped breathing.'

Caroline stared at her in stunned silence, her head swimming. She felt as if she was going to pass out. There had to be some ghastly mistake. Yesterday Roy was having his last swim in the pool before catching their flight and today he had stopped breathing.

'Mrs Hayim,' the sister continued, 'his condition is stable at the moment and he's breathing with the help of a ventilator. We're taking him up to Intensive Care and you'll be able to see him there.'

Ventilator! The awful reality of the situation at last dawned on Caroline. That had been Roy in the cubicle, not some unknown man for whom she'd felt vaguely sorry.

'I know that this must be a terrible shock for you, but we're doing everything that we can for him. As soon as we have more news we'll let you know.'

Caroline nodded, unable to speak as tears welled up in her eyes.

'I'll send in one of my nurses to sit with you,' the sister said, standing up and taking a quick glance at Caroline before she slipped out of the room. Within minutes, a young nurse appeared, carrying a tray with tea and biscuits. Caroline tried to give a watery smile of thanks and sipped the scalding liquid absently, glad of the quiet presence of the nurse but scarcely hearing her conventional words of reassurance.

The sister returned to ask her for a list of all the foods Roy had eaten over the previous forty-eight hours but, when she tried to think, she discovered that her mind had once again gone blank. Nothing. She could remember Saul's salmon but little else. How was she going to manage without Roy, when she couldn't even remember simple things like that? What was she going to say to the children waiting for some news at home? Was Roy going to pull through or . . .? The alternatives were so unthinkable that she couldn't even contemplate them.

'Roy . . . Roy, are you awake?'

Caroline was calling his name but her voice sounded strange as if she was far away, muffled. Where on earth was she standing? Roy tried to tell her to come closer, to speak up, and he opened his mouth to form the words. Nothing happened. No sound came out. In fact he wasn't even sure that he had moved his lips at all. Perhaps he was still asleep.

Wake up Roy and answer her, he chided himself. He tried again but once more failed to produce any sound. He couldn't open his lips. Indeed, he couldn't move at all.

He lay there, stunned. What was going on? A growing feeling of panic surged through his body and he tried to sit up and look around. Again . . . nothing. He couldn't sit up and his eyelids were locked shut. He was aware of the bright lights of the ward and dim shadows moving around the bed. One of them presumably was Caroline. Roy lay quietly for a minute, trying to acclimatize himself to this new situation, Caroline's voice piercing through his consciousness like a comforting beacon.

'Roy, can you hear me?'

Yes, I can hear you . . . but I can't move. What have they done to me?

He wanted to scream out but no longer had control of his body. Caroline touched him gently on the arm and he could feel her closeness.

'I'm here, Roy,' she said quietly, 'are you all right?'

Roy wanted to laugh hysterically at the question. He'd come in with a bad attack of food poisoning and since then it had deteriorated to the extent that he was completely paralysed. How could he be 'all right'. His body felt as if it had seized up totally and was no longer obeying any commands that he might give. Although not aware of inhaling and exhaling breath, he seemed to be getting air. He couldn't open his eyelids, having to be satisfied with the general distinctions between bright and dark so that Caroline's voice floated vaguely into consciousness like some disembodied voice.

Moreover, it felt incredibly frustrating, to have someone talking to him and not being able to reply at all. Trying to turn his head in the direction of her voice he again found himself trapped, immobile. Now Roy grew really agitated and angry and threw all his strength and will behind moving his hands. He lay still, exhausted, waiting for a reaction.

'Look his thumb is twitching slightly,' someone said. 'He must be conscious.'

Slightly! Is everybody going blind around here. I feel as if I've almost thrown myself out of the bed!

It only gradually dawned on him that he hadn't moved much at all. What had felt to him like a huge gesture was in fact barely perceptible to onlookers. It was as if his inner and outer worlds had been wrenched apart irreparably.

Maybe if I go back to sleep, then this ghastly nightmare will go away.
'It's me . . . Caroline.'
Her voice was deliberately loud and slow.
I know it's you. I'm not deaf! he fumed inwardly.
'Roy, it's going to be okay. Can you hear me?'
She sounded anxious and weary as she held his hand, pleading
with him to respond. He couldn't. Then he remembered the earlier
comment and strove to move his thumb again.
'Oh Roy, you can hear me,' and he realised that she was crying.
She stroked his hand gently and he felt tears well up inside him
as well, the anxiety of the recent events taking its toll. He wanted
to lie in her arms and weep. Then he discovered that even his tear
ducts had run dry. He couldn't even cry.

Caroline followed the doctor out of the room, shaking from the
sight of Roy lying there. Immobile and pale. He was covered in a
foil sheet to keep him warm, with tubes strapped up his nose and
connected to the ventilating machine. When he first moved his
thumb, she was overcome with relief and was still trembling as a
result.
'He's conscious,' she repeated to the doctor.
'Yes, Mrs Hayim,' he replied gently, aware that she was still in a
state of shock. 'It seems that Roy can hear everything that's going
on but can't respond at all, other than that slight movement in his
thumb.'
Caroline digested this fact in silence, her mind too numb to ask
any questions for the time being.
'Now, could you tell me exactly what Roy has eaten over the
past few days.'
She looked at the young doctor aghast, finding it hard to focus
on anything. He smiled at her kindly.
'Why not start with what you all ate last night and work
backwards?'
'Well we had salmon for supper,' she began hesitantly. 'My brother
stocked up in the fridge with cheese, French bread, smoked salmon,
cucumber and fruit to keep us going when we came back from
holidays. We all ate it and it tasted fine.'
'Contaminated food unfortunately often looks and tastes normal,'
he remarked.
'Then there was that terrible meal on the plane,' she continued.

'It smelt so awful that none of us could eat it and the stewardess threw it out. Roy did have a few mouthfuls of the rice and peas but then stopped.'

The doctor took the details of the airline and made a note to get samples from the batch. If it was food poisoning, that meal was the most obvious culprit, and if the contaminated food emanated from the airline, then the health authorities would have to be notified and all the remaining food on that particular airline would have to be withdrawn and closely scrutinised.

'On Saturday evening, we went out for dinner and Roy had avacado vinaigrette for starters . . . so did Alex . . . and fish for the main course. He didn't have dessert. Sunday morning was the usual breakfast – croissants, boiled eggs, orange juice, coffee . . . I think we all had more or less the same,' she ended, slightly confused but glad to have something concrete to focus on. It helped to clear her head and get her thoughts in order.

The doctor remained silent, wondering how much he should tell her at this point. In his late twenties, Dr Wolff showed all the promise of becoming a brilliant doctor and combined shrewd medical insight with a gentle manner and sensitivity, both in his dealings with patients and staff alike. Roy's symptoms had baffled them all at the Edgware General, so sudden and severe were their onset. Given the medical history, food poisoning did seem to be the most likely cause but the severity of the symptoms had never been seen before.

Several hours later, Dr Wolff had at last hit upon a possible diagnosis and rushed to the medical text book to confirm his sudden intuition. Botulism! A form of food poisoning caused from the neurotoxim Clostridium Botulism, which results in vomiting, abdominal pain, blurred vision, depression of the nervous system . . . the resemblance to Roy's symptoms was too close to be coincidental. Indeed, he was presented with almost a classic textbook picture and Dr Wolff felt a surge of excitement. To his knowledge, there had only been a handful of cases of botulism in Britain during the whole century and he was about to start treating one of them.

Here his brief-lived euphoria ended. If it was indeed a case of botulism, they were in trouble. The expert in this area was away on holiday and was not readily contactable. Furthermore, recommended treatment strategies were dodgy and focused mainly around an antitoxin which prevented any further deterioration in the condition only if given in time. Without the antitoxin, death was probable, if not certain.

Recalling these pessimistic predictions, Dr Wolff hesitated once more before speaking to the pale woman in front of him. Then something in her expression finally convinced him. There was an inner-strength there that told him she would be able to cope with whatever he had to say, and he looked at her steadily.

'Mrs Hayim, I have reason to believe that Roy is suffering from botulism. It's a form of food poisoning that is so rare that I've never actually seen a real case before. However, he resembles the textbook description too exactly to leave me, in any case, in much doubt.'

Caroline looked bewildered while he gave her a brief description of the illness.

'I've given him a drug to paralyse the system so as to make full ventilation possible and have taken blood samples to send to the lab in Colindale for testing.'

He paused, giving her time to assimilate the information before going on.

'The expert in this area is on leave at the moment but we're doing our best to contact him. In the meantime, I could give him the antitoxin to combat his symptoms.'

'Well, what's the problem?' Caroline asked, angry that the expert should be away this week of all the days in the year.

'The problem is that we normally like to confirm a diagnosis before starting treatment. The results from Colindale won't come through for another few days and . . .'

'And?'

'Well, to be quite honest, I don't think we . . . Roy . . . can wait that long.'

Caroline felt suddenly very weak as the full impact of his words sank in. Roy didn't 'just' have food poisoning any more and she understood at last that he was fighting desperately for his life. She looked at the doctor in despair and saw an expression full of quiet concern and sympathy. Instantly she trusted his judgement completely, knowing that she had little other option.

'What would you recommend then?' Caroline asked faintly.

'I'm not sure, but I think that the antitoxin may be his only chance. There's obviously a risk as there is with any drug but my gut feeling is to give it a try,' he said honestly, knowing that he had the full backing of his colleagues.

'Go ahead, then,' Caroline said quietly. 'Give him the antitoxin before the results come through.'

Dr Wolff smiled briefly and left to make the necessary arrangements. Caroline returned to Roy, taking hold of his hand and feeling again the tiny movement in his right thumb.

'They think you've got a form of food poisoning called botulism,' she said clearly, her voice betraying her only by the slightest of quivers. 'The doctor is going to give you an antitoxin which will make you better.'

She stopped, unable to go on and praying that the doubts hadn't penetrated through to her voice. He lay very still and at first she thought that he hadn't heard her. Then she felt the gentle move of his thumb, a movement that was to be their only means of communication for quite some time. Caroline wanted to take him in her arms and reassure him that everything was going to be all right, but had to be content with just holding his hand and guessing how he was feeling. Already the struggle to break through the frightening barrier that lay between them had begun.

How long am I going to be like this?

The thought pounded through his head relentlessly, unceasing.

How long?

He wanted to cry out for someone to give him the answer, his whole body screaming out for reassurance, but no one could hear him. He was trapped in a vice grip of a body that had ceased to function, except for his thoughts. He suddenly wondered how much they owed to the body and how much to . . . what? He groped around in his vocabulary to find an appropriate word and drew a blank. Spirit perhaps? Roy was unaccustomed to thinking of such matters, having always been too busy with the practical aspects of life to dwell too long on such issues. Not that his faith didn't provide him with much comfort, especially now when he could rely on few others for solace. None the less, questions like what is left after the body has departed never really interested him, having always reckoned that he would find out soon enough when he died.

Of his senses, his sight had gone completely but his hearing had become attuned to even the slightest sound as if to compensate. His thoughts were frighteningly sharp and clear but he could not move any part of his body. At times they were bland, detached from the terrible predicament in which he found himself while on other occasions like this one, they tortured him with nagging fears and doubts.

You're never going to walk or see again.

It was his deepest fear, more than even dying. Indeed the question of whether he would survive hadn't really occurred to him, and he doubted whether anyone really thought that they were going to die until the last moment, if at all. No, what bothered him more than anything, was the prospect of being disabled, forever dependent on others for every tiny thing. How much of the truth were they actually telling him, or were they shielding him from what they didn't feel he could cope with in his present state?

Caroline had slept in the waiting room for the first few days so as to be near him in case he needed her and much to Roy's relief. He couldn't bear it when she was absent, even for a few minutes. The day stretched on into night and he dozed fitfully, trying to remember what day it was. Monday? Tuesday? Wednesday? Already he felt as if he had been lying there for weeks. Monday had been one of the worst days of his life, Tuesday and Wednesday no better. What would tomorrow bring? Would there be a tomorrow?

The expert had arrived . . . at last. It had been difficult to contact him as he was on a golfing holiday and even though Dr Wolff had been in telephone communication to confirm diagnosis and administration of the antitoxin, he didn't see Roy until the Wednesday. Nor did he have much to add to the diagnosis given by Dr Wolff. Roy most definitely had botulism and was extremely ill.
    'Top marks for observation.'
    Caroline was annoyed that he hadn't arrived sooner even though he had the most laudable of excuses. Moreover, she had grown fond of Dr Wolff and trusted his judgement completely. Indeed, all the medical staff liked the young doctor, his cheerful manner brightening up even the most sobering of wards like Intensive Care. When he was on call at night he'd appear on the ward at six o'clock with a notebook or supper orders for the local Chinese take-away. Both Roy and Caroline were amused at the hours it took the nurses to make up their minds, unused to the luxury of eating other than the rather bland canteen food.

'Hello Roy.'

It was Caroline and he was overcome with relief. She was the only one he could rely on to tell him the truth and he racked his brains as how to communicate his concerns to her.

'How are you feeling? Are you in pain, Roy?'

Her voice was concerned and quiet, and he tried to pick up the undercurrents. Despair? Did she think that he was going to be like this permanently? Was she putting a brave face on things for his sake? It was so hard to tell, and he remained undecided while he tried to work out the answer to her question.

I'm not exactly in pain but uncomfortable all over. The pain is more aches and cramps because I reckon the nurses aren't turning me enough. Now how on earth do I communicate that in squeezes?

It was a few days later and his thumb movement had progressed into a hand squeeze.

'Remember, one squeeze for "yes", two for "no", ' she prompted gently.

Yes or no? Oh I suppose, 'yes' my legs are aching to the point that it is pain now.

He squeezed once.

'Where is it hurting,' she asked anxiously, hoping to make him as comfortable as possible before she broke the news. 'Your chest?'

Two squeezes.

'Your arms?'

Twice.

'Your head?'

Twice. Roy was beginning to feel tired.

'Your legs?'

Once. At last!

'Nurse!'

Without wasting any time, Caroline was calling the nurse so that she could help turn him.

'We've been turning him every two hours,' the nurse said slightly defensively, as they lifted Roy carefully onto his side. 'Otherwise he'll get bedsores. Still, the good news is that we're renting a wonderful air bed just for Roy and it should work a treat.'

'Wonderful,' Caroline exclaimed.

'Very expensive too,' the nurse continued. 'You wouldn't believe how much it cost.'

'How much?'

She told them.

'My goodness, that much!'

'Yes. It's operated by remote control and you can inflate or deflate the bed to take into account the contours of Roy's body. It should be here some time today.'

'Do you hear that Roy?'

He squeezed her hand, not feeling terribly enthusiastic at all but didn't want to appear ungracious. Already Roy was beginning to resent any little change and experienced a vague panic at the prospect of shifting from the safety of his old bed. When she was happy that he was comfortable, Caroline repeated her conversation with Dr Wolff doing her best to explain the symptoms of botulism and to play down the significance of the antitoxin.

So how long?

She was talking quickly but hadn't answered his one burning question, cleverly skirting around it instead. Roy felt frustrated and uneasy, and was working out how to ask her something more specific when the air bed arrived. They transferred him with a minimum of fuss, ventilating him manually for the brief moment when they moved the ventilator.

'How does that feel now, Roy?' the nurse asked triumphantly.

Terrible. I can't believe that you're going to make me lie on this for long.

Caroline held his hand and repeated the question.

'Are you comfortable now?'

Two squeezes. *You've got to be joking.*

'Where does it hurt?' she asked patiently, listing all the parts of the body as before. This time, he squeezed once for at least half of them.

'Oh Roy, it's supposed to be helping you.'

It wasn't, and he grew more and more uncomfortable until the air bed had become the bane of his life. Caroline learned how to work the switches but it seemed to be a losing battle.

This is costing the hospital so much money and it's worse than useless. I've got to get back to my old bed. My neck's getting some support but the rest of me aches and I feel as if I'm hanging in mid-air.

The nurses tried to stick to the two-hour interval of moving him, a source of fierce contention with Roy who was often in agony after thirty minutes. Caroline pleaded on his behalf to be changed back to an ordinary bed but to no avail. The doctors insisted that once he got used to the air bed, it would be far more comfortable and would overcome much of the problem of bedsores. Roy listened to the conversation, fuming and feeling even more helpless. He knew that Caroline was doing her best but felt angry even with her . . . with everyone, including life itself.

Chapter Three

A STARTLING INCIDENT

ROY AWOKE suddenly to hear his name coming, of all things, from the radio. He thought he was going mad. Then he realised that it was Brian Hayes on Radio London and he was talking about him. Why on earth was he being mentioned on the radio? For a brief moment he thought that something had gone terribly wrong at the office . . .

'Botulism is an extremely rare illness, and one from which few people survive . . .'

Few people survive!

The words penetrated through to his consciousness with razor-like sharpness. *Few people survive . . . My God, this is serious. I knew that they weren't telling me everything. Does this mean I'm going to die, that they were lying when they said I was going to get better?*

He started to shake all over, facing death for the first time and not liking what he saw. *Few people survive.* The phrase rang through his mind like a death knoll. He wasn't ready to die; he'd far too much to do still. What about Caroline and the children? He hadn't even put his affairs in any sort of order . . .

When Caroline arrived in that morning she was greeted by rather worried-looking nurses. They knew that something had upset Roy on the radio and had promptly switched it off. How much he had heard was not known and it remained for Caroline to discover, slowly and painfully, what had happened.

'It's all right Roy,' she said soothingly, her voice steady and scarcely betraying her inner panic and anger. A fright like this could do untold damage to Roy, and the doctors had repeatedly stressed the need to keep him calm and relaxed. 'You know how the media exaggerate everything to create sensational news. You're going to be fine, Brian Hayes does not know what he is talking about. You know that unless something is sensational it's not news, just don't believe him.'

She's not telling the whole truth. She's covering up because she knows something.

'It's all right Roy,' she said soothingly. 'I've spoken to the doctors and they're positive about your recovery.'

He clung to her comforting words as to a lifeline, desperately wanting and needing to believe her. He had no choice if he were to gather together the energy to fight on, to keep trying. Without hope, the hard struggle to get better would have been impossible and the will to live itself unable to survive. He tried to calm himself down and listen to Caroline's news as to cards sent and telephone calls from friends but couldn't dispel the faint feelings of unease. *How much of the truth am I getting? Will I ever recover fully with no scars?* The brutal reality of botulism was at last making itself felt.

Caroline sat back, exhausted. It had taken the entire morning to convince Roy that the radio broadcast had exaggerated things and she still wasn't sure if she had succeeded. She felt furious that people could be so irresponsible and insensitive. It was only that morning that she had been asked to go on Breakfast TV. Didn't they realise that all Roy and herself wanted was privacy; they had enough on their plates without coping with badgering from reporters as well. The other day a journalist had knocked on their door and asked for a photograph of Roy. When they refused he had the cheek to try their next door neighbour, who promptly replied that if Roy's own family wouldn't supply one, his friends certainly were not going to.

From what little she had been able to find in the library, she gathered that botulism was indeed serious. Hardly any more reassuring to discover that very few people survived this devastating illness. The doctors were being very supportive and encouraging but she suspected that they were as much in the dark as she was.

'How long is it going to take?' she demanded of Dr Wolff that day after Roy had fallen into a fitful sleep.

'I honestly don't know,' he told her bluntly. 'We're breaking new ground here as I've never read of such a serious case; I'd be misleading you if I tried to fix a time limit on it.'

At least he had tactfully refrained from saying that Roy might not make it, she reflected wearily.

'So what do I tell him? I suppose you've heard about the radio incident this morning,' she said grimly.

'Yes, that was most unfortunate,' he agreed. 'We need to keep Roy as positive as possible and avoid frightening him with ideas of dying. That's why I don't think his brothers should come over just now.'

Roy's two brothers lived in South Africa and had just telephoned, having heard the news. Both wanted to come over immediately but Caroline had asked them to hold on. The doctors felt that Roy would only interpret their arrival as a sign that he was on his last legs and unlikely to recover.

'So what do I say?' she repeated desperately, wanting him to give her certainties, some hope to cling to, and yet knowing that he couldn't.

'Tell him that it will be weeks. In a few weeks we can say another few weeks,' Dr Wolff advised. 'It would be too much of a shock to tell him that we don't know how long. The recovery rate in people who have had a very mild attack of botulism could be fairly rapid once the recovery process has started but given the severity of Roy's symptoms, we just don't know. Once his recovery is triggered off we might get a better idea of how long, but until then we are absolutely in the dark.'

Caroline suspected that if Roy knew how long he was going to be in hospital, he'd just give up. Whatever happened, she had to shield him from the truth and a repeat of this morning had to be avoided at all costs.

Every function in Roy's body had become mechanised. He wore no pyjamas to allow for easy access to all parts of his body. They had inserted a urinary catheter, a heart monitor, a saline drip to prevent dehydration and even a feed line to his chest since his stomach was no longer absorbing food. On top of that, the nurses suctioned phlegm out of his lungs, already affected from inhaling vomit and subject to recurrent bouts of pneumonia, to avoid infection from the ventilator, they changed the filter and tubing every twenty-four hours.

As Caroline gazed at her husband, kept alive by machines which had taken over his body, she marvelled at the achievements of modern medicine. And yet would modern medicine be able to cope with the inner Roy, his struggles and fears, his lack of interest in the home, the children, even the office?

Caroline kept him informed of all she could think of at home and within the hospital and explained each medical procedure, speaking with painstaking slowness, even though she knew that his hearing was unaffected. She even managed to intuit where he was aching, how he wanted to be moved, what he wanted her to bring in from home. One squeeze of the hand (he had progressed from the movement of his thumb to the weak bending of his fingers) could say more than ten words and his whole body seemed to give out moods – one moment despair, another mirth. It was as if they had taken a major leap and were communicating on an entirely different level, one which neither of them really understood but which started in a realm far beyond that of language and ordinary body signals.

And yet there were those days when they were both so tired that they couldn't 'talk' at all, where all communication broke down because neither of them had the energy to make that quantum leap. On those days, Caroline was forced to resort to more practical methods, ones which the nurses could use if they had the time. They devised a simple code, such that Caroline called out each letter of the alphabet, waiting for a squeeze of the hand before starting again to get the second letter of the word. It was slow and laborious but it worked and letter by letter each word was built up. It allowed Roy to express himself more fully, especially at night when Caroline had gone home and he needed to make himself understood.

'A . . . B . . . C . . . D . . . E . . . F . . .'

Caroline methodically called out the letters, receiving a squeeze at 'F'.

'All right, F . . . G . . .'

The calling went on until she came to three of the letters F . . . E . . . E . . .

'Feel? Feet?'

Roy squeezed once, and they started in on the next letter. This time the letters were all towards the end of the alphabet and by the time Caroline had got the first three she was getting very tired. So was Roy and it was getting hard to detect his squeeze with accuracy.

'S . . . T . . . U . . . V . . . W . . . X . . . Y . . . Z . . .'
Caroline went through the whole alphabet and looked at her
husband in bewilderment.

'You didn't squeeze,' she accused him, slightly angry until she
noticed that he was equally agitated and shaking.

Caroline gazed at him thoughtfully.

'Did I miss out a letter?'

Twice.

'Did I miss out your squeeze?'

Once.

'Oh, I'm sorry,' she said. 'Let's start again and I'll go a bit slower.'

Caroline bit her lip with annoyance and called out all the letters
again.

'A . . . B . . . C . . . D . . . E . . . F . . . G . . . H . . .'

Once.

'H . . .' she repeated with joy.

Once.

Her mind filled with horror as she had forgotten the word's first
letters. She glanced at Roy who waited expectantly, the awful truth
only dawning on him gradually. He was clearly furious, shaking
more than she'd ever seen him in the last few days, but the harder
she tried to remember, the more her mind went blank.

'Oh Roy, I'm sorry.'

She could feel hysterical laughter bubble up inside her even
though she was trying at the same time not to cry, so tired did she
feel. Everything had suddenly become too much for her.

'Look, let's start again,' she said bravely, knowing that he was as
worn out as she was.

'A . . . B . . . C . . .'

It seemed like an age until he squeezed once.

'I . . . T . . . C . . . ITCH!' She shouted out the word. 'Feet Itch.
You want me to itch your feet, is that it?'

Once.

'I'll get a notebook at lunchtime so that I can write down all the
letters,' she promised. 'At least this won't happen again.'

As soon as Roy had dozed off, Caroline slipped out to get a
notebook. Glad of something tangible to do, she savoured the warm
September air, enjoying the break from the antiseptic smell of the
hospital. Life seemed to be so normal out here that she felt somewhat
disorientated. Her own world had been turned upside-down over

a matter of days and yet here were all these people rushing around, completely unaware of her upheaval. Not even the weather acknowledged their tragedy, and the sky was a pale azure, bright and sparkling in the brilliant sunshine.

Caroline lingered outside as long as she could but knew that he would want her there when he woke up. She bought the notebook and a newspaper and hurried back, suddenly convinced that something terrible had happened to him and that she should be there. Heart pounding she raced into the hospital entrance and swiftly down to the Intensive Care.

'Roy . . . is he all right?' she asked breathlessly of the sister.

'Why, yes.' The sister looked surprised at Caroline's sudden agitation and followed her uncertainly to where Roy lay, wondering if she had missed something serious.

Roy was still sound asleep, and Caroline collapsed into the chair beside him, feeling drained and miserable. She couldn't stand the strain much longer, the uncertainties and fears that he wouldn't make it through the night, or from one hour to the next.

'Are you all right, Mrs Hayim?'

The sister was watching her curiously, and Caroline felt embarrassed. How could she explain her sudden irrational fears outside the newsagent, her conviction that she was going mad at times with anxiety, her inability to even remember what day of the week it was?

'Yes, I'm fine thank you.'

Roy started to stir and she turned gratefully to the bed, glad of a diversion to take the attention off her. While the nurses arrived to turn him, she used the time to pull herself together, to briefly recharge her batteries for the long slow battle ahead.

Their next stage was to divide the alphabet into four; A–F, G–K, I–R, S–Z. Caroline called out the different sections and then focused letter by letter on that section. It quartered the time element and the entire process became less laborious. Once written down, she tried to make sense of the letters which ran into each other, putting in the natural breaks.

Where is Caroline?

The question was poised on his lips almost from the moment he awakened, his heart sinking if he did not find her in her familiar chair by his bed. Roy couldn't open his eyes but he knew that it was morning, as the bright daylight penetrated even through his closed eyelids. He had survived another night, another long struggle where he slept sporadically amidst tortuous cramps and laboured breathing. Even if he did manage to drop off for half an hour, he was inevitably woken up by the nurses to be turned or monitored in some way. It amazed him how many small checks they constantly needed to do − blood pressure, heart rate, breathing − he had lost track of which test was which, but knew that the nurses would be guaranteed to come just when he managed to drop off to sleep.

And then, when I do need them they're never around, he thought disgruntedly. *You'd think there'd be someone nearby, especially since Caroline isn't sleeping here any more.*

She had spent the first few nights sleeping on the hard sofa in the waiting room, but had eventually been persuaded by the doctor to go home. Roy knew that he was being unreasonable to expect her to suffer sleepless nights and back pain, but he dreaded the moment when she left each night, leaving him to make his needs understood as best he could.

'Morning Roy.'

He recognised the voice immediately and was relieved. It was that young West Indian nurse, a cheerful girl who was experienced enough to make him feel comfortable whenever she was giving any treatment.

'Time for your morning wash.'

He knew, just as he knew that blood tests, injections and physiotherapy would follow. It was the same inevitable ritual every day. Once the night shift left, the hospital routine would roll on relentlessly, irritating in its inevitability but comforting none the less to Roy, who clung to any familiar landmark that he could to offset the frightening illness that had shattered his old way of life.

The nurse came closer to his bed and gently pulled back the covers. And another nurse came in with hot water and Roy felt himself grow tense.

Will it be hot enough? Yesterday it was lukewarm . . . bordering on cold, and they didn't even warm their hands before touching me,

'Okay Roy, we'll start with your arms and chest. Ready?'

He felt the wet cloth gently on his arms and he slowly relaxed. It was warm. The nurse was gentle but thorough, washing him all over and turning him gently onto his side so that she could wash his back. None the less, it was with relief that they pulled up the covers again when they had finished and Roy could settle back in peace. A week ago he wouldn't have believed this could have happened and that he could accept it so calmly. Two strange women washing his naked body and he unable to do anything. It was such an invasion of his privacy and yet he had suffered that already to such a degree that he no longer felt as if his body belonged only to him. It was almost shared out, with the medical team having by far the greater input at the present time.

The nurses chatted while they remade his bed, telling him about themselves and their families. They even asked him about his holiday and his own children, phrasing the questions so that he could answer yes or no. It was nice to be included and Roy felt human again, as if he was really contributing to the conversation. He'd forgotten what it was like to talk about normal things and to have nurses address him rather than talk about him like an inanimate object.

Then came the woman from the blood laboratory who proceeded to prick his already raw fingers in search of more blood. He dreaded weeks of this, fearing that he would have no skin left on his hands if she were allowed to pursue her determined course of action. Still, at least it helped to pass the day and filled in the hours before Caroline arrived. The nurses turned on the radio, keeping an eye on what channel he listened to after the distressing incident the other day, and he lay there listening to some rather nondescript music.

Tired after all the activity of the early morning shift, Roy lay quietly, his ears pricking up when he heard someone switch off the radio.

Caroline?

'Hello Roy,' she said gently, kissing him lightly on the cheek. 'How was your night?'

All the anxiety and tension slipped away miraculously at the sound of her voice. He could now relax and let Caroline take over. She looked after all his needs and concerns, taking as she did the time to work out exactly what he needed. For the time being, at least, he could leave it all up to her once more.

The results from the Colindale Laboratory had at last come through and confirmed Dr Wolff's intuition. Of the six mice who had been injected with Roy's blood, the three who had not taken the antitoxin were dead. It was highly probable that Roy would

have followed a similar fate had Dr Wolff not followed his gut
feeling and Caroline felt relieved that Roy was in such capable
hands. The admiration was mutual and, after watching Caroline
spend half an hour getting one sentence out of Roy using the
alphabet method, Dr Wolff burst out laughing.

'My God, you really are a remarkable couple!'

Caroline blushed with a mixture of pleasure and embarrassment.
She didn't feel that they were remarkable; after all what choice do
you have if someone you love becomes so ill? You just do what has
to be done, rather than questioning things all the time.

None the less, the strain was already showing and she looked pale
and tired. As much for herself as for Roy, she had taken the doctor's
advice and forbidden any visitors. Friends and relatives still called
in but sat in the waiting room, waiting for her to come to give
them the latest report on Roy's condition. It was extremely touching
and she felt heartened by so much support and concern but at times
found the effort of talking to even good friends quite a trial.

Roy was just about to begin his physiotherapy for the morning,
leaving Caroline for a while to check up if anyone was in the
waiting room. She pushed the door open slowly and went in,
looking round hopefully at the empty room. Then she saw her
Uncle David and Aunt Rita sitting there quietly in the corner of
the room, sensible, calm and reassuring.

Caroline suddenly felt this tremendous wave of emotion overcome her and she burst out, 'I can't cope. No one knows when, if
ever, he'll get better. What am I going to do?'

'What you're doing . . . nothing more. What other choice do you
have?,' they said. 'You have to keep going, not only for yourself,
but also for the sake of the children.'

Caroline nodded miserably.

'I know. It's just that it is such a terrible burden. I have to be so
careful what I say, I can't let Roy know when I am upset, I can't
lean on him. I've got to put on a brave face all the time, it's just so
exhausting. I feel as though I've got the troubles of the world on
my shoulders and I don't know how much longer I can go on like
this.' Her voice trailed off unevenly and she stopped for a moment
before going on. 'I can't even let Basil and Derek come from South
Africa in case Roy panics. I don't think he realises how serious the
whole thing is.'

'Don't underestimate him,' her uncle warned. 'I suspect Roy does realise but is coping the best way he can, by blotting it out of his consciousness and focusing on where he is, here and now.'

'Why don't you get a couple of hours' rest,' her aunt suggested. 'We could sit with Roy and call you if anything happens.'

'No, you're very kind but I'm afraid I can't, he hates it when I'm not there, but thanks for being here I feel much better now that I've had a good cry.'

'You won't be much use to him if you collapse.'

'I know, and I'll be careful. I'm going home at night now but it's hard for Roy when I'm not there as no one has the time to go through his elaborate communication system.'

Caroline really did feel better off for unburdening herself on her aunt and uncle. She no longer felt so alone, so needing to appear in command with Roy and the children totally dependent on her.

'The doctors suggest that we don't tell Roy the whole truth as he might give up in despair altogether. It could be months before he's better . . .'

She looked miserably at the kind faces of her aunt and uncle and decided that things weren't so terrible after all. Somehow their presence had a calming influence and she felt a renewed strength to go back and deal with Roy.

'We'll be here if you want to come back and talk about anything,' her uncle told her, giving her a quick hug before she left for the ward.

Caroline had the latest cards and letters from home and spent the rest of the morning, reading them out to Roy.

Caroline drove the eight or so miles home. It was not exactly cold but it was dark and a light drizzle made a wet film on her windscreen, that kind of frustrating rain that wasn't heavy enough to put on the windscreen wipers but was sufficiently moist to have to peer in order to see the road ahead. As she turned onto the main Edgware Road, she suddenly became aware that the summer had raced by with alarming haste. The Indian summer had turned to autumn overnight, and the brilliant sunshine of the first week had given way to mists, strong cold winds and early morning frosts.

Her mind returned to the road as she slowed down to accommodate a crossing lorry and she was surprised to notice that she was nearly home. The journey had already become totally familiar, so that she did it as automatically as the well worn route to school or to their local shops. The mist was growing thicker and prudently she switched on her headlights. In some ways the summer had ended abruptly for them all. From basking in the warm Mediterranean sunshine, where time seemed to stand still and responsibilities belonged to another land, they had all been rudely awakened, plunged into autumn without so much as a moment's notice or time to acclimatise themselves.

Home! She pulled into the driveway and parked her car carefully in front of the house. Slowly she gathered her bags off the floor of the car, taking her time as she switched off the headlights, undid her seatbelt, locked the doors. She needed those few moments before going into the house to be swamped down by a new range of problems, this time from the children, and not Roy. They were all coping surprisingly well but she knew that they too were under a tremendous strain. Little warning signs told her that they were as anxious as she was – Rachel had already been in detention twice since the start of term for disrupting the class; all were liable to fly off the handle at the slightest provocation and were clingy and demanding when she came home. She tried not to lose her temper, knowing that it was their way of dealing with their anguish, and felt increasingly guilty that she wasn't at home more.

Her mother was looking as exhausted as the rest of them and wouldn't have been able to cope for much longer. Even with friends doing the shopping for them each day, sharing the school runs and taking the children for afternoons and weekends, there was still an awful lot of work to be done running the household. Since Roy had become ill, the telephone hadn't stopped ringing, and her mother systematically made a note of every call and whether or not Caroline needed to ring them back. After greeting the children, this was her first task and she prayed each evening that the list of calls to be returned would be short.

Then came her own lists – shopping for friends to do, organising the school runs for the next day, things that Roy wanted brought into the hospital . . . it seemed to be never-ending and she longed just to collapse into a hot bath and her bed. Then time to tuck the children up . . .

Her mother glanced anxiously at her face, noticing the dark shadows under her eyes.

'How is Roy today?'

It was a question they all hated facing, knowing that the news was never good and usually bad. No change in his condition was a godsend but rare, and Caroline would desperately search for some funny story to tell them when she came, something to lighten up the usual tale of setback after setback. He seemed to be making little if any progress but was managing to stay reasonably stable on the whole.

'He's fine,' Caroline eventually replied inadequately, before changing the subject. 'How have the children been.'

'Fine.'

They stared at each other and smiled, Caroline putting her arms around her mother and giving her a big hug.

'I'd never have been able to manage without you,' she whispered, and went upstairs to kiss them all goodnight before starting on her chores.

They were waiting for her, and she felt another pang of guilt, knowing that they needed her at home now more than ever. She couldn't be in two places at once and Roy was so insistent, so demanding that she stay at the hospital all day. She reassured them that Roy was getting stronger, omitting to say that his temperature had started to rise that evening and the doctors feared yet another setback. Alex studied her face carefully but she deliberately kept her expression calm, noncommital and discussed their plans for the next day. Louise had invited the girls to help her bake after school, Alex had his football practice and Eric wanted them all to spend the Saturday with him.

'Will you come too, Mummy?' Naomi asked, knowing it to be impossible.

'I can't. Daddy needs me at the hospital, but I'll collect you from Eric's in the evening if you like.'

It was a small consolation and she knew it.

'I've been finding out about botulism,' Alex announced proudly.

'Really?' Caroline's interest quickened as she herself had pored through the medical journals and had come up with very little, nothing more than the bits she had gleaned from Dr Wolff. Certainly nothing about how long the illness lasted or how to treat it.

'Yes . . . nothing much, though. There have been four or five cases this century. Two died.'

He let the words drop like an accusation. The children had been begging to see Roy from the moment he went in but Caroline felt it was too soon. Roy looked so weak and pale that it could upset them further. She had put them off with reassurances that Roy was making steady progress but couldn't manage any visitors at the moment, even from his own family. It worked initially but now they were beginning to imagine the worst and demanded to see him. It was doubtful whether their imaginings were any worse than the reality but Caroline realised that it wasn't fair to keep them in this uncertain state of apprehension. Roy was going to be like this for quite some time and they were going to need to come to terms with it. Better to start now rather than shutting them out any longer.

Strangely enough, Roy had agreed with her. Although he refused steadfastly to see any visitors, he too recognised the need to touch in with the children, if only for a short visit, and suggested that she brought them in on the Sunday.

Sunday arrived. It was pleasant to have company on that dreary drive to the hospital. The children chatted freely while she pointed out the now familiar landmarks. It was only when they drove in the hospital entrance that they fell silent, as if of one accord.

Would he be all right? Would he even be there? It was her permanent fear, even though the nurses had promised over and over again to ring her if there was any dramatic change in the night. Now the children had to face those same fears as she; more than anything she had wished to shield them from that anguish but knew it to be impossible. Roy was too important to all of them for his presence not to be sorely missed every moment of the day.

Now, as she left them in the waiting room while she checked that Roy was awake, she wasn't too sure. She had got used to seeing him like this, paralysed, rigged up to every possible hospital machine, inaccessible. Yet she could still remember the shock when she first saw him lying under the foil sheet. How on earth would the children react when they saw their father in a such a state?

She told Roy that they were all here and went back to the waiting room. Alex followed her first, with the two girls trailing behind. They walked shyly into the room and stood at the end of the bed. Silence. All three blinked in horror and stared at the man in the bed.

'Daddy,' Naomi wailed and Caroline sensed the tears in her voice.

Alex was doing his best to put on a brave face but couldn't take his eyes off the ventilator, staring at the machine in disbelief. Before coming in, Caroline had prepared the children by describing what the ventilator and intravenous drips were for, but no description could anticipate such a formidable array of hospital equipment. Then, as if pulling himself together with a sheer act of will, Alex walked up to the bed.

'Hello Dad,' he said shyly. 'It's me, Alex.'

He put his hand into Roy's, who squeezed it once for 'Hello'. Alex glanced up at Caroline with a surprised look, his eyes glowing with pleasure and the two girls rushed forward.

'And me, Daddy,' Rachel chatted excitedly.

Caroline stepped back, relieved that the ice had been broken. She encouraged each to take his hand in turn. It was heartbreaking to watch them, their three earnest faces fixed upon Roy, making a superhuman effort to be cheerful and pretend that nothing was wrong. Roy enjoyed the visit but Caroline noticed how tired he was becoming with the strain of responding to each child in turn. Dr Wolff came in quietly towards the end of the visit and Caroline turned to him gratefully, glad of the diversion. When the physiotherapist arrived, he ushered them all into the waiting room and sat with them trying to explain to them about Roy's illness with the hope of alleviating some of their fears.

Caroline was grateful that she had taken the precaution of asking Saul to join them in an hour. He planned to take them all out to lunch, after which Caroline would return to Roy and Saul would organise an afternoon's entertainment for the youngsters. That way, some of the shock would be diffused and they wouldn't have to stay around the hospital for the whole day.

Saul arrived promptly at midday.

'All ready for an outing you'll never forget,' he grinned, noticing the lines of tension around Caroline's mouth and guessing how difficult she had found it. The children looked pensive but relieved to have confirmed for themselves that their father was still very much with them, but reluctant to leave the hospital. They could, however, now visualise the ward where, day after day, their parents were, and could relate on a concrete level to the illness and Roy's treatment. Nothing more was needed for the present and they were persuaded to join their uncle.

'Food first,' he announced firmly. 'Then the Science Museum and maybe boating in Hyde Park.'

After the children had gone Caroline sat by Roy's bed holding his hand and looked back on their fifteen years of married life.

'Do you know, I don't think we've ever had so much time to

'speak' to each other and discuss things as much as we are now, even though it's rather one-sided. We always seem to be in such a hurry. We've lost the art of conversation. When you get better, we'll spend more time talking to each other and discussing things.' Roy squeezed her hand twice (once for yes, twice for no) – there was that indomitable spirit and sense of humour – nothing was going to change!

Chapter Four

THE NATIONAL HOSPITAL FOR NERVOUS DISEASES, QUEEN SQUARE

Leave Edgware?

IT HAD to be some sort of ghastly joke. Roy received the news in stunned silence, a horrified feeling creeping through his bones as the words sank in.

What do you mean, leave Edgware?

He was shouting out the words inwardly, unable to fully believe what he was hearing.

'It's for your own good,' Caroline continued helplessly, aware that she was sounding like a school headmistress. 'You need to be in a hospital which specialises in patients on long-term ventilation. The physiotherapy facilities are meant to be much better and the staff more experienced in dealing with . . . with your kind of illness.'

She had been going to say 'long term' but managed to stop herself in time. None the less, her words of reassurance sounded like a half-digested regurgitation of a medical treatise and she knew that it would fall on deaf ears at best and formidable rage at worst.

I don't want more experienced nurses, he thought icily. *I want people who know me, who understand how to make me comfortable, here, in the Edgware General where I'm comfortable.*

Caroline surveyed the still body of her husband rightly interpreting the stony 'silence' as seething fury and panic. He wouldn't even squeeze her hand to indicate that he had heard. *I don't want to leave Edgware.* The irony of the situation suddenly dawned on him; he, who hated hospitals, doctors, pills . . . begging to stay in intensive care!

'Roy, we don't really have a choice so don't work yourself up into a state about it,' Caroline said firmly, deciding that plain speaking was probably the most effective course of action at this stage.

There was no point in handling him with kid gloves any more, not if he was to be ready to go within an hour. They had deliberately withheld the decision from Roy until the last moment, knowing that he would panic and not want to be disturbed from the familiarity of the Intensive Care unit, the now-recognisable voices of the nurses, even the air bed about which he still complained daily but was an accustomed feature in his cloistered world.

'I'll pack your things and will be following behind the ambulance,' she continued bravely. Caroline had also been staggered at the news but realised the necessity of a transfer. She was terrified that Roy wouldn't survive the journey, or that if he did, the staff at the new hospital would be less sympathetic, less competent.

'It should be here in an hour.'

AN HOUR!

Roy almost choked in horror. *How can they just spring this on me? They must have known well in advance so why couldn't they tell me, give me time to get used to it.*

'I know it's short notice but . . .'

Short notice? What an understatement.

'We didn't want you to worry too early,' she continued, no longer feeling up to the task of breaking the news to Roy.

At that point Dr Wolff walked into the room. 'Ah Roy,' he said heartily, ignoring the warning signs, the taut body, the refusal to communicate with his hands or anything else. 'I see from your cheerful expression that you've heard the news.'

Dr Wolff paused, taking in a deep breath before carrying on. In spite of himself, Roy listened, the sardonic humour of the doctor causing him to smile grimly to himself.

'We're obviously devastated to be losing you but feel that the move will be for your best interests.'

He's presenting it as a fait accompli, Roy thought irritably to himself. *So why all this discussion and show of being a democracy?*

'What's up to you is where. The choice is between the National Hospital in Queen Square or Northwick Park Hospital in Harrow.'

Harrow!

'They're both good and they both have a vacancy, so it's really your decision but you'll need to decide fairly promptly.'

I most definitely do not want to go to Harrow. It's miles away; how would Caroline ever get there each day? It's much more convenient to be in Queen Square.

Dr Wolff took Roy's hand as he continued to talk in a soothing voice. 'So if you could let me know which one you want, I could begin to make arrangements . What about Harrow?'

Most definitely not. Two squeezes.

'Right, so I take it that it's Queen Square then?'

One. *Thank God for that.* Roy sank into the pillow, relieved to have escaped from an exile miles away that would clearly be difficult for Caroline.

Dr Wolff smiled to himself as he left the room, while Caroline looked on in amazement. He made it seem so easy. She tentatively started to gather up Roy's belongings, waiting for a continuation of the conflict that had been going on before Dr Wolff arrived on the scene. To her surprise, Roy seemed quieter and anxious to 'talk'. Putting aside the overnight bag, she held his hand and spent the time trying to interpret what was going through his mind, answering his questions as best as she could.

'Yes, I promise that I'll be there to help you settle in,' she reassured him. 'The anaesthetist and one of the nurses will go with you in the ambulance so you don't need to worry. You'll be ventilated manually on the journey.'

As if on cue, the anaesthetist arrived, and Roy became the centre of much attention and activity. For his part, he was intent on ensuring three things – that he was indeed not going to Harrow, that he would be ventilated properly and that Caroline would be there. Nothing else really interested him and he seemed oblivious of the administrations of the nurses – fixing up an intravenous drip for the journey and a portable ventilator. As they lifted him onto a stretcher, he grimaced inwardly in recollection. It was Monday 14 September, exactly two weeks after the admission to Edgware. He was still completely paralysed, unable to breathe on his own, unable to perform any of the normal functions of his body, unable to open his eyes – his life had been turned completely upside-down. Now, it felt grimly as if the first chapter in his illness was closing and he awaited the next stage with extreme uneasiness.

The journey was as terrifying as he had anticipated. The quiet solitude of his cosy recess on the ward was rudely shattered by the noise and bustle of the Edgware General on a Monday morning.

As the ambulance team navigated Roy through the long corridors
of the main hospital, he could hear the stream of activity going on
around him, the clatter of heels on the lino floors, the crashing of
trays and swinging of door after door as they raced past the wards.
It was quite definitely unmistakably hospital, its sounds, its atmosphere of ongoing emergency . . . here all were on red alert, and a
quiet period was viewed suspiciously as the lull before yet another
storm rather than a normal course of events.

Then another shock as he hit the outside and was lifted onto a
stretcher into the ambulance. The blast of cold air assaulted his
whole being, and he felt numb and shivery, surprised by the cold
of the September day. Was it only two weeks ago when he had
travelled back from holiday in short sleeves and sandals?

'Squeeze my hand if you are feeling uncomfortable,' the anaesthetist told him, her calming voice bringing him abruptly back to the
present.

Within seconds, they had transferred him to the portable ventilator and his predominant fears in relation to his breathing were
gradually subsiding, so efficient and quick was the exchange. None
the less, as the ambulance started up, he realised that he could expect
torment from another area. They drove at full speed through the
busy traffic, siren blaring with unnerving vigour, and Roy felt as if
every part of his body was being battered from all sides. The whole
vehicle vibrated as they screeched around corners or bounced over
the uneven surfaces of the road, and he ached with an intensity that
he hadn't imagined possible.

'Soon have you there,' the nurse remarked reassuringly.

Better late than never, he wanted to shout, fearing that he could
scarcely bear such discomfort for much longer. Besides, he was in
no mad hurry to reach his new surroundings, and all his earlier
misgivings were reawakened as he listened to the conversation of
his companions. The National Hospital for Nervous Diseases at
Queen Square sounded huge, impersonal, and even more daunting
than it had been described by Dr Wolff.

The ambulance turned a corner at high speed, causing Roy's
body to lurch the other way.

To take his mind off the pain, Roy tried to imagine the route
they were taking. As if tuning into his strategy the nurse kept up a
running commentary as to where they were, and images flooded
into his mind. He knew the area reasonably well, having driven

along those streets himself, looking at new properties for clients. *Does Caroline know how to get there?* He prayed that she was following close in her car, although he doubted whether she would be able to keep pace with the ambulance.

Once around Queen Square and a final lunge to the left as the ambulance drew up in front of the hospital entrance and they came to a halt. The driver switched off the siren and Roy savoured the few seconds of blissful silence and stillness before the hectic scramble of unloading him began. It was all done with breathtaking speed that he scarcely felt the cold air on his face before he was inside the building.

Queen Square. New nurses, new doctors but still hospital, with its familiar noises. All he needed now was Caroline to pave the way much as a scout prepares the ground for the advancing army. He strained to hear her voice amongst the many all talking around him at once but couldn't.

'We're gong to lift you onto the stretcher now, Roy, and take you up in the lift,' the nurse who had accompanied him was saying. 'It seems as if your bed isn't vacant yet so you're going to a temporary place for the day.'

Temporary! Does that mean I'll have to move again? His throat was tight with anxiety as he lay grimly on the stretcher, unable to even express his growing concerns to anyone nearby. At last they reached the lift and he heard the steady purr of the elevator as they ascended to the next floor. The doors opened and he heard her voice.

'Hello.'

It was all she said but one word was enough to dispel all the anxiety for the time being, and relief flooded through every vein in his body. *Caroline! She's here to accompany me through the rest of this nightmare of a move.* Within seconds, his whole mood changed and he began to breathe more easily.

They lifted him onto his new bed and he lay there, overcome with delight. *A real bed!* The air bed had been well and truly left behind, despite certain last-minute vague promises to send it over to Queen Square with Roy. As he sank into the firm springs of the mattress, Roy felt suddenly faint and drowsy. He tried to stay awake, having so much wanted to ask Caroline something, but quickly gave up what was clearly a losing battle. Within minutes he was sound asleep, confident that Caroline would still be there when he woke up.

While Roy slept, Caroline looked around the ward with mixed feelings. In some ways it looked very different to the Edgware General but, like Roy, she immediately recognised familiar landmarks and found them comforting. It was as if the hospital blueprint stamped itself everywhere so that regional differences were swept aside in the face of a predominant uniformity.

After the Edgware staff had settled Roy, they left with the ambulance crew. Caroline was sorry to see them go, feeling lost without their familiar faces. She glanced around her at the ward, everyone busily rushing around and looking as if they knew where they were going. Everyone but her, that was, and she felt insecure and lonely. It was like being a child again at your first day in a new school; sheer hell until you learned the ropes.

Caroline pulled herself together and walked purposely down the corridor in search of a nurse. She wasn't a child and she had Roy depending on her to make sure he got the best treatment. She had to make it her business to find out where everything was, and quickly, rather than waiting shyly and politely in the background. She hesitated perceptibly before knocking on the door of the nurses' station and, suppressing the grimace that was creeping over her face, pushed the door open.

By the time Roy awoke, Caroline had discovered all the public landmarks, such as where to make tea, the toilets, the shop, as well as the names of the ward sister and the doctor who would be replacing Dr Wolff. He was suctioned quickly and efficiently by the nurses and they put water-filled gloves under his feet to prevent bedsores. They were certainly very experienced here and Roy's previous anxieties began to evaporate. Where there were difficulties, these were quietly smoothed over by Caroline who became his main link with the outside world.

The first clash took place within days between Caroline and a male nurse, and Roy was only aware of the scene after the event. This particular male nurse had left Roy in a position that made him feel uncomfortable. Needless to say, Roy communicated his distress to Caroline who went in search of the nurse for assistance.

'Don't tell me how to do my job.'

Caroline started back as if he had struck her, and gazed into a pair of hostile and arrogant eyes. She took a deep breath and forced herself to be assertive, even though most of her wanted to run away from the confrontation in confusion.

'I beg your pardon?'

She spoke quietly and politely, prepared to give him the benefit of the doubt and pretending that she hadn't heard his first rebuke.

'I said, don't tell me how to do my job,' he repeated haughtily. 'He was fine when we left him, so if you'll excuse me, I'm really rather busy at the moment.'

He started to move off but something in her look checked him. No longer feeling embarrassed or shy, Caroline was now just plain furious. Without so much as bothering to make a curt rejoinder, she turned her back swiftly on the man and stormed off to see the sister in charge. It was many weeks before that particular nurse appeared on the ward again, and it later transpired that he had made similar insensitive comments to relatives of the other patients.

Fortunately, that incident blew over almost as quickly as it had arisen and generally didn't spoil their reception at Queen Square. Roy formed close attachments to several of the nurses. Hakeem, recently arrived in London from the Middle East, kept him amused with a steady chatter about buying a new car, while the ward sister was experienced, knowing exactly how to make him comfortable. So did Nadin, a pretty twenty-eight-year-old nurse whom Roy trusted implicitly.

So why isn't she married then? Roy pondered, having already asked the question of Caroline with no satisfactory reply. She promptly accused him of male chauvinism and tartly replied that Nadin was obviously too sensible to fall into that trap. Roy hastily dropped the subject but continued privately to wonder. He longed to be able to see again rather than floating in a sea of disembodied voices.

Then I could judge properly, he thought before checking himself promptly. *How many of our rash judgements are based on visual input alone, and I'm the worst culprit for that. If nothing else, this illness will have taught me to use my hearing as well, and it's amazing how much you can pick up from just the tone in someone's voice.*

Roy's favourites were on the night shift, whom he had regularly and they thus got to know each other, particularly Mohammed, and Caroline was amused to see the close tie of friendship that sprang up between the huge black nurse and her husband. Whenever Roy had a difficult day, Mohammed would be told to settle him for the night. It was indeed a comfort to Caroline who could drive home in the knowledge that he was in good hands. Whenever Mohammed went away on a few days' leave, there was so much disappointment and unease that Caroline offered to stay overnight in the hospital.

'Most certainly not, Mrs Hayim,' the ward sister announced firmly. 'You need your rest or else you'll end up in here alongside Roy. He'll be fine and it's good for him to learn to trust other people.'

She was right but it didn't stop Roy from complaining bitterly as the time approached for her to leave. To him, replacements were bad news, and new nurses never seemed to understand exactly how he needed to be moved. His complaints were but a transparent camouflage to hide his fear and she felt torn by guilt as she made her way home along what was quickly becoming as familiar a route as the one to the Edgware General.

Roy woke up shivering and knew that he was in for another fever. He groaned, unable to face the usual paraphernalia that went with these recurrent infections and fevers. Sometimes he was given an anaesthetic if they had to change something like the site for his feed line and this played havoc with his thinking capacities.

His mind would wander and his sub-conscious fears would take over. It must have been when he was either under an anaesthetic or when he was too weak to think clearly that he found himself dozing off. The next thing he realised was that one of the nurses was asking him downstairs to her flat for coffee.

'It'll do you good to get out for a bit – I'll wheel the bed back whenever you want.'

Still feeling quite groggy but glad to escape the claustrophobic atmosphere of the ward, Roy agreed and she took him downstairs to her flat.

As they went into the flat Roy suddenly became aware of a noise coming from the living room. The nurse appeared not to notice and pushed open the door, wheeling the bed in. The room was full of black men with hostile expressions on their faces. Before he knew what was happening they pounced on him, pulling the sheet off him and shouting his name.

Who are these people? How do they know who I am?

Panic-stricken, Roy tried to attract the attention of the nurse, but she was encouraging the men and laughing nastily at Roy's discomfort.

For God's sake, get me out of here.

'To hell with you,' the nurse shouted. 'You came here out of free choice so it's up to you to take the consequences.'

He pleaded and begged her but she walked out, leaving him sandwiched between two sweating and naked strangers. The nurse returned shortly with a black couple carrying a child. They too directed their unfriendly stares at Roy and seemed to be enjoying the punishment.

What have I done wrong? Where am I?

The man nodded and moved slowly towards Roy, who suddenly realised that he was going to throw hot water on his private parts. Only the baby begged for mercy but she was ignored by her parents. Just as the man was beginning to pour the water, Roy regained his consciousness.

On another occasion Roy found himself in an underground passage surrounded by a gang of angry youths. The nurse accompanying him was chatting to a long-lost friend and ignoring Roy's distress. Suddenly one of the youths produced a knife and tried to cut the tube connecting Roy to his portable ventilator. Just as the youth started to slice the tubing Roy was aware of being back in his ward. *How did he get back?* He lay there for a few moments trying to gather his wits together. It must have been another nightmare.

Later he understood that anaesthetics can bring about hallucinations but, at the same time, he felt as if he was losing his grip on reality.

He was sure that she was getting later. The night shift had long gone, he'd had his bed wash, blood tests, injection of heparin, even physiotherapy. Now the doctors were doing their ward round and she still hadn't come in; she was usually there to act as interpreter. It wasn't the day when she went to see Naomi's teachers which always delayed her about half an hour.

The doctors were all there. The registrar, Dr Colebach, senior house officer Dr Finnerty, his own consultant Dr Wiles. They gathered around the bed to discuss the case . . . case! *Funny to think I'd become a case.* It made him feel so small and insignificant, no longer a person but a thing to be poked and prodded as they did the routine tests. He had managed to identify each voice with a name now and knew who had a gentle manner, cold hands, bad breath. And yet, he wouldn't know any of them if he met them in the street; he had no idea what they looked like at all.

What is keeping her? The nurse was doing her best but she was misinterpreting most of what he wanted to ask the doctors, too impatient to spend the time spelling out each individual word as Caroline did.

'So how are you feeling today?'

It was Dr Wiles speaking.

Awful. Everything aches and I've a terrible cramp in my right leg.

He waited for the nurse to take his hand so that he could communicate this but she didn't. Instead she tried to answer the question herself.

'He's had a good night and slept until six o'clock,' she said, while Roy lay there fuming.

How dare she answer for me? How does she know what I'm feeling.

Dr Wiles took Roy's hand and asked him.

'Are you feeling more comfortable since we changed your feed line, Roy?'

Well yes, although I wasn't altogether happy with that terrible hallucination the other day.

One squeeze.

'Do you mind if we take a quick look at your chest?' he asked courteously.

You're going to anyway, whether I mind or not, aren't you?

Roy felt like a small child rebelling against parental authority but was feeling angry that Caroline was so late, and peeved at being handled like an inanimate thing.

Taking his silence to mean assent, they started the examination. A slight movement in one leg was all they found. Little else.

Caroline arrived, breathless. She gave no reason for being late and launched into a conversation with the doctors, barely saying hello to him. He suddenly felt very small and insignificant and alone. His greatest pleasure was when she walked through that door. She made him feel more secure, more relaxed and was the only one willing to take the time and effort to communicate with him. More than that, she provided a link with home, with the children and even the office, who rang almost daily to keep track on his progress.

When the doctors left, Caroline gave him a quick kiss and asked how he was. It was too late, the damage had been done and Roy felt too annoyed and hurt to respond. She quickly guessed what was wrong and patiently went over old ground.

'Roy, we've discussed this before with the nurses,' she said defensively. 'They feel that I should come in a bit later to fit in with the visiting hours.'

Rubbish, I don't give a damn about visiting hours. You're only using it as an excuse.

He lay silent, in too much of a sulk to respond.

'Besides which, I need to spend more time at home sorting things out and spending time with the children at the weekend. You're busy in the mornings with physiotherapy and everything else; surely an hour either way doesn't make much difference.'

It did, but Roy knew he was on a losing battle. The nurses had told him in no uncertain terms that Caroline was going to start coming in a bit later. That ridiculous story about visiting hours had been their official reason but they also told him that Caroline was looking worn out.

'She needs more time to herself, Roy, or else she's going to become very ill,' the ward sister explained and he had fumed, wishing that they wouldn't interfere.

I need her here.

The issue had been unresolved at the last 'discussion', but he realised after today that he in fact had no choice. Caroline was going to start coming in later and there was nothing he could do about it. He could no longer control or influence anything in his environment. The helplessness of his situation filled him with a black depression and he lay quietly, too apathetic to bother any more, too miserable to care what happened to him. When Caroline returned, she knew that she had her work cut out for her that day.

'Mum is still there being wonderful,' she remarked, 'but I'm not sure if she's strong enough to cope with three lively children for much longer.'

Roy stiffened as he went through one of the most dreadful scenarios.

Is she going to tell me that she can't come in so often?

'Perhaps we should try to get someone in,' Caroline continued comfortably.

'Maybe it would help if we got an au pair.'

It most certainly would.

He knew how difficult it would be for Caroline to have someone living in with them. After years of au pairs, mainly on account of Naomi, they had finally got rid of their last one a year ago. Now, Caroline would have to go through all the problems of agencies and interviews. Still, there was no way that her mother would cope and it meant that Caroline could give him her undivided attention; he was beginning to stop fooling himself that he would be better in a day or so; weeks or months was more likely to be the case and he was going to need Caroline every bit of the way.

The Australian au pair arrived. Try as she could, Caroline could not overcome a tremendous feeling of guilt, knowing that she should be spending more time with the children. It seemed so unfair; she wanted to be there when they came home from school, to take them to their clarinet or piano lessons, to cook the dinner, to do all the things that she enjoyed doing for them, instead a complete stranger was now doing it all for her and in her own house. Never before had she felt so completely torn, pulled by the demands of Roy who competed ruthlessly with his children for her time.

WHAT ABOUT ME!

She wanted to shout the words from the top window of their house so that they reverberated all over the street, words she knew she could never express, not simply because of her strong sense of guilt, but because they would be wasted on the people who mattered. They were still children, all of them, demanding, unyielding, growing up, needing her to be strong and without weakness so that they could shelter from this storm beneath her protecting wings.

After what seemed like hours, but in fact was probably only minutes, the nurse reappeared and noticed his distress.

'Are you all right Roy?' she asked gently, and he tried to speak, still forgetting occasionally that he was no longer able to utter a word.

Please, please turn me once more.

The nurse gazed down at him, trying to guess what was wrong. She held his hand and started to go through the usual line of questioning.

'Is it your feet that are uncomfortable?'

He squeezed twice.

'Your legs?'

Twice.

'Your back?'

Twice.

Roy tried to think clearly. He'd just been turned from his side to his back but his whole body ached. If she could turn him on to his other side, he might be able to twist his good leg underneath which would give him more support.

'Your arms?'

This is going to take ages; how am I going to tell her that I want to be turned again quickly.

'Your chest?'

Roy started to despair as she worked her way through each part of his body, always starting with the feet as a matter of course. He wondered if this was also part of hospital policy! He sensed her growing impatience as she failed to locate the source of his discomfort anywhere.

'Look Roy, we've just turned you so you should be comfortable,' she began, unable to hide the note of exasperation in her voice. 'You normally prefer being on your back, don't you?'

Normally, yes, but not tonight.

He squeezed twice.

'You don't?'

She sounded thoroughly confused now.

'You want to be turned again?'

Eureka!

He squeezed once, exhausted from the effort.

'But, we've only just turned you. You'll have to wait for a bit longer.'

Good God, you can't just leave me like this.

'Look, I'll come back in about twenty minutes and see how you're doing.'

He couldn't believe what he was hearing. His whole body tensed up violently and he started to shake. To his relief, she took pity on him and called her colleague to help turn him onto the other side. He managed to get his leg tucked in so as to take the bulk of his weight. Already it felt much more comfortable and he settled back, knowing that he would probably be able to sleep now.

It was then that he noticed his ear. So intent had he been on getting his leg in the right position that he hadn't noticed that his ear was bent forward, taking the full weight of his head onto it.

It was mildly uncomfortable to begin with but became more and more painful as the minutes ticked by. He tried to move his head but gave up, knowing that he was having no effect whatsoever.

Roy lay there, inwardly seething with frustration.

How on earth am I going to get them back?

His thoughts circled wildly inside his head but he could come up with no easy answers. To distract himself from this new torture, he started up a conversation with himself.

What if they don't come back for another two hours? How will I ever stand this pain?

Don't be stupid, they never leave you for as long as two hours.

But how will I tell them that it's my ear that's in agony?

As if on cue, the nurse stuck her head around the door. 'All right, Roy?'

He started to shake, girding up his last bit of strength to attract her attention.

'Roy, we can't turn you again; we're really busy this evening and do have other patients besides you.'

He continued to shake.

'Is there some part of you that's giving particular trouble,' she asked with a sigh.

Once.

'Is it your feet?'

Oh hell, why don't they start somewhere else.

His ear was burning at this stage and he wanted to shout aloud. None the less, he started to squeeze twice in response to her questions.

'Your legs?'

It seemed to be interminable. The nurse reached the head at last.

Once.

Then she spied the bent ear. 'Gosh, that must have been uncomfortable,' she said.

You're not kidding!

I am not sure what percentage of body weight is contained in the head, but it certainly feels like a good fifty per cent. The relief of having his ear released was so great that within seconds Roy was relaxed enough to be sound asleep.

Caroline rang in every morning before coming in to see how the night had been. He was vaguely irritated to learn that the sister always said that he had been 'fine' even if it had in fact been a grim ordeal. Somehow it helped when you were suffering agonies to

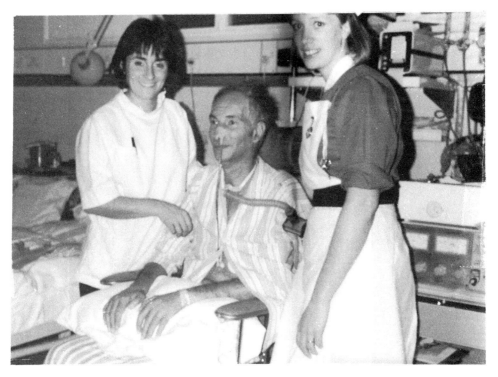

ABOVE: Roy with physiotherapist Julie and nursing sister.

LEFT: Family group of Rachel, Roy, Naomi, Caroline, Florence and Alex.

ABOVE: Sister Rachel, Roy and Mr Li.

RIGHT: Caroline and Roy today.

have everyone know. Although Roy could understand why the sister tried to reassure Caroline he wished that she could be a little more realistic; indeed, it had been a long time since he had felt anything even approaching 'fine'.

After his bedwash, Roy noticed that there was a new nurse on the ward and he instantly became jumpy, scared that she would be sent over to him. One of the most anxious times was when new student nurses were shown around the ward while the sister tutored them, 'on the wing' as it were. Particularly when they came to the ventilator, a contraption that he regarded with such reverence that he disliked anyone going so much as within a foot of it. Having a lecture delivered right by his bed, a step by step account, of what to do should an emergency arise and the ventilator stop working, was hardly conducive to his peace of mind. To his daily prayers Roy added the fervent wish that should this emergency arise, none of the student nurses would be on his patch.

Especially the one he encountered that morning. Having assisted with the bedwash, she was left to tidy up and make sure that Roy was warm and comfortable. She was obviously very nervous and kept making conversation, forgetting that he could only reply with yes or no and only that, if she held his hand to interpret the squeezes. Roy bore it all under sufferance with reasonable good humour, wondering who would want to become a nurse anyway.

What on earth is she doing?

His rambling thoughts were rudely interrupted by the latest antics of the nurse. She was trying to pull his teeth out!

'I can't seem to get them out,' she exclaimed breathlessly.

Thank goodness for that, he thought, totally bewildered by the assault.

'They're very well made, almost look real.'

What is she talking about?

He groaned inwardly. It was the last straw.

The girl gave another tug on his teeth.

'Nurse, what are you going? Can't you see they are Roy's own teeth!', said the Sister. 'Oh, poor Roy, just to think that you could have gone home without your teeth!'

Thank you very much, thought Roy. His teeth had always been his pride and joy. Even though he was 49 years of age, he only had about two fillings. In better times he had always been so meticulous about brushing his teeth, always buying the most expensive toothbrushes and insisting that the children would brush their teeth as thoroughly as he did. Lose them indeed!

'I'm sorry, Roy,' the sister said apologetically, hoping that he wasn't going to get worked up into an agitated state. 'So many of the patients have false teeth that she must have thought yours were too. They look so perfect it's hard to believe they're real.'

Flattery is no way to appease me, Roy thought in amusement, thoroughly enjoying himself now.

When Caroline arrived Sister Rachel told her what had happened, but she was pleased to find Roy in good spirits. He was so changeable, that incident could have easily gone the other way. Armed with the list of well-wishers who telephoned the evening before, cards, the daily papers and a box of tapes sent in by friends, she settled herself beside the bed, ready for the long day ahead.

They had both slipped into an easy pattern. First news of the children, phone calls and any messages that she needed to pass on to him. They would read the papers with Caroline selecting parts of articles that she thought might interest him. She always had to be careful not to make them too long, for his attention span and concentration was still fairly limited.

Following that, some music tapes – Arthur Rubinstein's Chopin was one of their favourites, Beethoven and Brahms. Instinctively drawn towards the Romantics, their rich harmonies were undoubtedly a necessary antidote to the prosaic reality of the hospital and the endless grim medical procedures. One of their visitors had also left a tape by John Arlott, an account of cricket from 1920 to 1970, with a description of all the personalities involved over the five decades. Just the sort of thing that appealed to Roy but Caroline generally excused herself once she put it on.

Indeed, the tapes allowed her a few minutes' reprieve. They kept Roy entertained, his mind off the discomforts and pain that had become part of his daily existence. He was able to experience Dickens's *Nicholas Nickleby* for the first time, while they both enjoyed a recording of the life and times of Siegfried Sassoon, followed up by Caroline reading some of his stories.

None the less, there were days when time just dragged, dawdled and inched along one painful second after the other. The routine, on one level so comforting to Roy, also felt like a chain, a rut in which the boredom of each day was surpassed only by the sheer discomfort that he felt for many of his waking hours. He tried to think back to the time when he took his body for granted, ignoring it for the most part until it demanded attention, such as coming up to mealtimes. Think as he did, the past had become one hazy memory, the future an uncertain realm where the extent of his recovery was still unknown.

Chapter Five

THE STORM

NOW HE could afford to take nothing for granted, not Caroline, not his health, not even the ventilator which was placed protectively beside his bed. *What if it broke,* he wondered on one of his bad days? *Would I just slowly suffocate or would someone notice?*

Roy didn't have to wait long for the answer to these questions as his very worst fears were soon realised during the October hurricanes that took Britain literally by storm. That evening the winds picked up in intensity, howling and battering at the walls and windows of the hospital in an angry tirade. Towards nightfall, these gusts reached such a strength that it was difficult even to think. It was as if a raging savage beast had been unleashed, bent on wreaking as much havoc as it could on town and country alike. Trees were ripped out of the ground, crashing on unsuspecting travellers underneath, their roots pointing up to the air in a gesture of outraged surprise. The media issued storm warnings, cautionary words that came rather later, much as closing a gate after the horse has bolted.

The staff on the ward were full of chatter and excitement; how would they get home, would their cars parked around Queen Square be safe, would they get any casualties brought in here, given the reports of injuries and deaths all over the country as a result of trees falling on cars.

None of this was of any interest to Roy. He experienced a momentary twinge of irritation when he found it difficult to summon a nurse to his assistance and promptly blamed it on the distracting influence of the storm. For his part, he was warm and comfortable, already too detached from life to waste energy on the forces of nature which seemed intent on reminding mankind of their vital elemental power. The turmoil raging outside belonged to another world that he had left far behind.

Then the lights went out and the ventilator stopped. It happened so suddenly that Roy froze in disbelief. At first he was unsure what exactly had happened, still in that vague middle floating ground of shock where reality is suspended for the moment amidst an inner ringing in his ears, a dizziness and confusion in his head.

POWER CUT!

Someone shouted the words from the direction of the nurses' station and they cut across the darkness like a spear travelling at full speed. Unable to duck, the two words hit him full in the chest and he imagined his lungs caving in.

This is it . . . the beginning of the end.

He was strangely calm, almost relieved that the stress and struggle of the last month was finally over. He was tired of it all and wooed by the peace of unconsciousness, tempted just to let go and slip into oblivion.

A small voice, stirring from the depths of his very being, whispered that this was not to be so, refusing to allow him to go without a last fight. As if in a delayed reaction to the shock, the panic awakened in him and crushed the alluring voices. He began to shake violently aware for the first time of the sudden flurry of activity going on in the ward. The nurses sprang to the bedside of their charges, and Roy heard the calming voice of a male nurse, reassuring him that everything was going to be all right.

Now, once more, he desperately wanted to live. The brief moment of dallying with death, of being seduced into a darkness, a peace, was over and he lay there taut and frightened. Roy was gradually awakened to the awful enormity of the situation and the fact that he was incapable to do anything about it.

Immediately the nurse started to ventilate him manually. It had only been seconds between the transfer from the ventilator to the manual pump but it felt like hours. His heart was pounding as the adrenalin pumped through his body, and he felt a certain euphoria, a sense of having come face to face with death before finding himself snatched back again just in time.

The crisis was handled with efficiency, speed and no fuss. Shortly afterwards, the emergency generator came on and the ward soon seemed to be back to normal.

What if Caroline can't get in tomorrow, if the roads are impassable?

The floodgates of fear were now opened and his mind filled with details, insignificant worries, scenarios of Caroline being delayed, beseiged at home for hours, days . . . Having faced the ultimate terror, he crashed back down to reality in a suffocating accumulation of small worries, his only way of diffusing the trembling and his palpitating heart.

Then, suddenly unable to cope with the endless awful possible outcome of the storm, Roy tried to focus on reality once more. He strained to hear what had happened and discovered that the roads were like an obstacle course. People were being advised to stay at home unless their business was urgent. Unable to prevent it, his mind drifted back again once more to Caroline.

Please let her see this visit tomorrow as more than urgent. At this stage, he was unable to even entertain concern at the thought of her driving in such conditions. All he knew was that it was vital that she came in. Nothing else mattered. Even though the nurses reassured him that the power would return shortly and that the emergency generators would stay on for days if necessary, Roy remained on red alert, his inner agitation matched only by the raging storm outside. With the approach of dawn he lay there, tense, listening for any news of Caroline.

The same time as usual, Caroline arrived. Relieved to see that the power was back on, she sat down beside Roy and filled him in on the havoc caused by the unforeseen storm. The roads were strewn with trees and she had left home earlier than usual, having to take a different route on account of road blockages. With Caroline beside him, Roy was in the mood to learn more about the storm and listened to her chatting away with interest. Safe, cocooned within the confines of the hospital bed, he was content to enjoy it from a distance, glad that he didn't have to face it himself or battle back through the devastation to get home. For the time being, he had all he needed around him.

If there had been any doubt before, there was none now. Autumn had most definitely arrived. By mid-morning there was a howling gale outside and visitors arrived looking harassed and windswept, their hair in disarray, their coats speckled with rain. Moreover, the wind had a biting chill to it, a grim harbinger of winter. As relatives filed through the double doors of the hospital main entrance, the papers in the reception area fluttered and fell onto the floor, and the hall was filled with another fresh blast of the cold air.

One floor above reception, in the Intensive Care unit, Roy had lost the capacity to be affected by heat or cold and was causing much anxiety amongst the medical team. His temperature had soared as a result of infection from the feed line and it had to be changed yet again. He lay, receiving blasts of cool air from a fan to lower his temperature, while he simultaneously shivered as if freezing with the cold.

'Some more wet towels please nurse,' the doctor said looking anxiously at his patient.

Caroline sat, ashen-faced beside the bed, concerned at being in the way but unwilling to leave his side. It was another of those 'setbacks', a phrase she had come to fear and dread. Whenever his temperature went up, the doctors set in motion a range of medical procedures to stabilise his condition again. First the x-ray of his chest to see if his lungs were clogged up with phlegm, then wet cloths, antibiotics and the painful effects of these. She hated the whole process almost as much as Roy did.

'Mrs Hayim, could you step outside for a minute while we take an x-ray?'

Caroline rose wearily from her chair, the familiar routine started. *Oh God, not the x-ray.*

Roy groaned visibly as they lifted him up to put a plate behind his back. Once in position, they all sprinted outside as if they'd just left a ticking bomb by his bed.

What about me? What damage is it doing me if you lot can't even stay in the same room, he wanted to shout, sick of the lot of them. Angry, irritated, it was none the less a relief when they all returned and lowered him back onto the bed. He simply hated being left alone. Then they covered him with wet cloths and all his earlier misery returned, as his body shivered with the cold in spite of his high temperature. He awaited the injections, the next purgatory on the agenda, with increasing irritation. As if it wasn't bad enough being sick they had to add to his torment, so much so that he dreaded the treatment more than the actual fever. The final trial to his patience was inevitably the blood tests. He had developed an antipathy to both the painful procedure of finding a vein and the woman from the blood laboratory, despite the fact that she tried her best to cheer him up as much as possible. She would spend a harrowing time trying to find a vein that had not collapsed from which she could take a sample.

With the initial steps taken, the antibiotics followed on. Here Roy knew real discomfort, for these were injected into veins in the back of his hands. Within days at best, these veins would become sore and swollen and new sites were frantically searched for. It was excruciating and Roy suspected that his pain threshold must have risen dramatically over the past days; with each new sufferance, previous agonies seemed almost bearable by comparison.

Perhaps if I pretend that they weren't swollen and sore, they could continue to pump the antibiotics in the old sites for a bit longer. Pointless really, and his despair increased tenfold as he remembered that he couldn't move his hands properly, let alone hide them from medical inspection. At times he felt it would be easier to be left to die than going through this battle for life . . .

Caroline watched Roy anxiously. His face looked almost grey and he didn't seem to be responding to any of the treatment. She sat by his side until late that night, ringing her mother to say that she might not be home. Waiting. A slight shift downwards in his temperature, some sort of sign, please, to show that he was overcoming yet another fever, another setback.

This time Roy appeared to be sinking visibly before her eyes, his skin taking on a deathly pallor. She couldn't believe it. They had come this far and she had accepted that it could take many months, but that he would be well one day. This would be so unfair, to die from a fever when he had survived so far one of the worst recorded attacks of botulism.

She glanced up, sensing someone standing beside her. It was an unfamiliar doctor.

'He doesn't seem to be getting better,' she said nervously.

'No, his temperature is still very high,' he admitted. 'The infection hasn't cleared. We're going to have to do a transfusion of whole blood.'

Aids! It was the first thought that came into her head and she looked horror-struck. The doctor seemed puzzled by the intensity of her gaze and continued reassuringly.

'It's all right. It's just a routine procedure and he'll be fine afterwards.'

'No, it's not that,' she stumbled, uncertain how to put this so that she didn't make a fool of herself.

'I'm just, well, worried that the blood might be . . .' her voice trailed off as she looked at the doctor, comprehension registering on his face as he understood what was going on.

'Contaminated?'

'Yes,' she nodded, relieved that he knew what she was talking about but now more anxious than ever. 'We've heard so much about Aids and blood transfusions that you can understand why we're nervous.'

'Of course,' he smiled, 'but I can assure you that the blood we use is carefully checked and tested for the HIV virus before leaving the central blood bank.'

Caroline consulted with Roy before coming to any decision. Neither of them felt happy at the prospect despite the doctor's reassurance, but it didn't seem that they had any choice. Without the transfusion, it was doubtful whether Roy would pull through. With it, at least there was a chance. She told the doctor to go ahead and sat down wearily by the side of his bed. This was the second decision of a life-and-death nature that she had been forced to make since Roy fell ill. How many more hurdles would there be?

Roy had become a long-term patient. The initial shock of the time around admission had gradually worn off and the fraught struggle of the first few weeks at last had lost some of its intensity. Although he was still seriously ill, Roy's condition had stabilised sufficiently to allow the medical staff to ease slightly on their close vigilance. The sense of living on a razor's edge, of never knowing whether he would survive the night and be there the next day, took longer to leave Caroline, but gradually she too allowed herself to relax just a little, to sit back and take a few days' breath.

For Roy, this shift demanded new strengths of him, and he became restless and irritable in spite of his steady slow progress. Most difficult of all was coping with the enforced passivity and dependence, a state totally alien to his hitherto capable masculinity, somewhat domineering and at times aggressive. He had been a partner in his own business, the head of his household, an active member of the Jewish community. Energetic, forceful, choleric, staying long in one place had never appealed to Roy and the idea of spending weeks in a hospital bed would have been suggestive of hell itself. Yet, here he was, condemned to exactly that fate with no way of knowing how long, if ever, complete recovery would take.

Total stillness. Not inner stillness, for his thoughts raced inside his head much as he had moved through life prior to his illness, but a stillness none the less. He could no longer take refuge in outer activity, could no longer avoid his feelings by burying himself in work, physical exercise, even language. For the first time, Roy Hayim was brought face to face with his soul life and it was painful, perhaps as painful as the illness itself.

It was a time when he turned to his faith to help him find that inner strength. Uncomfortable though it was, the enforced silence of his body allowed him to renew his belief in God, and he was able to reconnect fully with His healing powers. It helped Roy to get through the hours of frustration, the profound passivity enforced on him by his paralysis, the deep fear he felt of dying, his utter dependence on Caroline. Through all the pain and feelings of sinking irretrievably into a deep abyss, he held his faith in God before him. It kept him alive in his thoughts, amidst the despair and doubts, and provided him with hope and inner strength.

Indeed, his thought life was the only part of him really active. All his life he had seen himself in terms of what he had achieved, where he worked, lived, what he did. This was *him*, or so he thought, a man who acted in the world and lived with the effects of his deeds. Suddenly he was no longer able to act other than in the most minimal way, and yet he was still very much there. His thoughts were louder and clearer than before, and Roy suddenly realised how large a part the thinking life actually played in an individual. It was as if every other part of man was limited, subject to physical ageing and disease – except his thoughts. In these alone, one was truly free, immortal, unlimited.

No longer fettered by the restrictions of his bodily life, Roy gave free reign to those very thoughts. All notions of going back to work shortly had long ceased to exist. None the less, the office was still very close in his consciousness, fuelled by the weekly visits from his partner Eric. Roy worried and fretted, wondering how long the office would go on supporting his family while he lay languishing in hospital, but found Eric a tremendous support. One of his first steps had been to reassure Caroline that she need not worry about the financial side of things.

Early one morning while he was lying there, Roy dreamed up a whole new plan for the office. It was like taking a few month's sabbatical in that he at last had time to step back and look seriously at his position in the business. He had been aware of an increasing dissatisfaction before the holiday and wasn't happy with his role in what was becoming a large business. Positioned in the office, full-time, doing all the negotiations, answering the telephone, listening to everyone's moans about why their properties weren't being let . . . all the day-to-day mundane stuff that distracted him from looking ahead and exploring new projects. It was about time that he stepped out and let the younger people deal with all that irritation. He was nearly fifty and could bring much more to the office by capitalising on the experience he had gained over the years.

Caroline's recent words that he hadn't learned to delegate came to mind and he pondered on them seriously for the first time. Maybe he should delegate completely, creating a new role for himself and handing over the routine work to his junior partners. The idea of being a public relations man had an appeal he wouldn't have believed years ago. He could go out to visit prospective clients, bringing stock in and encouraging people to instruct the firm to let or sell their premises.

It was an exciting thought and he longed to write things down and to talk to Eric. Impatiently, he waited for Caroline, wondering how he was going to communicate all of this to her. Then suddenly he checked himself. It wasn't important that it got written down and approved of straight away. Better by far to reflect on it a bit longer rather than rush in impulsively as was his wont. After all, he had day after day to do just that, to contemplate and meditate over whatever he pleased. Feeling rather strange, Roy tentatively tried out his new resolution and didn't insist that Caroline acted as his make-shift secretary the minute she came in. Instead, he hugged his plans to himself and developed them over the following weeks. It was a new approach for him but one that felt good and feasible for the day when he returned to normal life.

The daily rhythm, the rituals, the set times for doing particular tasks over others – all these became of prime importance to Roy. Without them, the days would have drifted into timelessness, merged one into the other in an unending flow of time and left him unsupported and rudderless. Instead, the hospital routine was his scaffolding, holding him together and providing meaning and structure to his existence.

It was also his prison. Deviations, however small, aroused such a panic in him that they were avoided at all costs. He was too brittle to be flexible, too ill to be able to adapt to uncertainties. Instead, he clung to the healing power of rhythm and order, resenting any disruption and expecting the whole world to conform and go along with his needs.

Comfort became his life value, replacing even love or family responsibility. Like a new god, it made itself felt in every aspect of life, often working against Roy's recovery rather than with it. Roy had become thoroughly embedded in hospital culture.

Over time, Roy's nerve endings began to sprout new attachments of the muscles and his body functions returned, one by one and painfully slowly. Indeed, for the first few weeks there had been little, if any, change in his condition but then improvements were suddenly perceptible, giving new hope to all. One young Chinese registrar took a particular interest in Roy's progress. He had written his thesis on botulism and was gratified to be able to compare Roy's recovery with the traditional textbook picture described in his manuscript. Regarded as something of an oracle on the subject, this doctor pontificated about botulism to all who cared to listen, telling Roy that without a doubt his eyesight would return 'any day now'. Unfortunately, his value lay far more in the hope that he inspired and kept alive in Roy and Caroline than in the accuracy of his predictions and 'any day' was at that time still in fact several weeks away. When Roy did finally open his eyes, his young friend was genuinely full of joy for him but sheepishly admitted that he would have to alter his thesis.

This was perhaps the most significant function to return and it appeared in a relatively dramatic way. Roy could always tell the difference between day and night as the light penetrated through his closed eyelids.

Several days before his sight returned, he noticed a narrow slit starting to open and excitedly called the doctor to show him this new development. Everyone waited with baited breath to see what would happen when he was able to open his eyelids completely, praying that the eyes wouldn't have been damaged and that he would regain full sight again.

One morning, in mid-October, as the grey dawn light filtered through the window into his room, Roy opened his eyes. He was alone at the time and lay there, stunned. Not expecting it to happen so completely overnight, he feared that it was another one of those hallucinations and nervously awaited his black persecutors to reappear. None came and his eyelids remained open.

Roy lay on his back so that he was facing the window expanding the full length of the wall and looked. *Colour!* It was the first thing that he observed and it flooded his very soul with a warm healing fullness. He feared that the vision would disappear but it stayed fixed, allowing him to drink in its splendour. Up until that moment, he hadn't realised how much he missed colour and how he had taken it so much for granted in the days before his illness. Despite the cold greyness of the London dawn, and the fact that he was still seeing double, there was a breathtaking array of colour. The red and gold of the autumn trees, the red tops of the post office vans seen along the bottom edge of the window. The dazzling glare of the rising sun, the birds sitting on the window ledge as they began their dawn chorus . . . it was sheer pleasure to be able to connect once more sight and sound together, sounds that he had come to be so familiar with but which felt slightly disembodied and unreal.

For those first few minutes, Roy just lay there, absorbing the world into his being and finding it beautiful as he saw it as if for the first time. Then his thoughts started to awaken, to take hold of this new faculty that had been absent for so long, and he began to imagine who might live in the properties across the road. He knew them to be a publisher's office, having read about it in the papers just before going on holidays, and toyed with the idea of investigating who might own the other one and whether it was due to go on the market.

The day nurse entered to give him his bedwash, and immediately noticed that his eyes were open. The delight and relief, after all the inaccurate predictions of the Chinese registrar, were contagious and Roy soon began to feel immensely pleased with himself.

'Good morning, Roy,' a cheerful and familiar voice greeted him and he looked up into the smiling eyes of the sister.

He was surprised to see how plump she was, but fortunately his speech had not returned at the same time as his sight, preventing him from blurting out any such tactless observation. Instead, he was able to absorb the world in silence, to observe without questions or comments. Roy felt an overwhelming sense of well-being, of completeness as the visual images complemented the already full auditory perceptions he had built up of the hospital.

He wanted to smile at her, to acknowledge how much support and care she had already given him so graciously but was still unable to respond in any way other than his hand. She understood and held his hand, noting that his gaze was still unfocused but conscious of the awakening expression in his eyes. Whatever happened with the other faculties, his sight seemed to be relatively undamaged and should, with time, return to normal.

While the nurses prepared for his bedwash, Roy's glance fell on the endless cards strewn all over the walls. He hadn't fully understood how many there actually were and was amazed and touched at the same time. Did he really know that many people?

He couldn't move his head and had to wait impatiently for the next time to be turned so that he could get a side view. Now he could see where the next bed was and the faces of the nurses washing him.

The bedwash over, Roy waited even more impatiently than usual for Caroline to arrive. He wanted to share the good news with her and was surprised that she hadn't already arrived. Then he saw the clock and concentrated on bringing the face into focus. *Ten o'clock, she was meant to be here by ten o'clock. Where the blazes is she?*

All his former delight and glory was quickly evaporating as he watched the hour hand on the clock tick around to eleven. He couldn't believe it; something dreadful must have happened.

Roy had been aware that Caroline was coming in later and later but hadn't known the extent. Indeed, from the way the nurses had talked about it, he had presumed that there was only about half an hour in the difference. Now he suddenly felt cheated and lay there fuming, watching the clock malevolently while his earlier pleasure evaporated rapidly. When she finally arrived, the sister saw her and came forward, a half smile on her face.

'Roy's opened his eyes – he can see.'

She let the simple statement sink in, amused at the mixture of emotions flitting across Caroline's face. Surprise, relief, sheer delight. Then, as she turned to go into Roy, she added mischievously, a twinkle in her eye, 'He can see the clock and he's furious – he wants to know why you are late!'

'Furious' was perhaps a gross understatement. After the intense joy that had quickened his heart when he first saw the world in the dawn light, Roy plummeted down into a seething rage, his only way of dealing with the inner turmoil of emotions. *How could she be late, and especially today of all days?* The fact that Caroline couldn't possibly have known that today was going to be a significant one never occurred to him, so angry and upset had he become. His whole body was trembling and it took her several attempts and much coaxing before he would even 'talk' to her.

'Roy,' she said patiently, refusing to let his ill-humour destroy her pleasure in the fact that he could see, albeit still in an unfocused, blurred way. 'I am no later than yesterday; I thought that we agreed that I should go home for an hour or so after the school run and before coming in. It gives me time to get through some of my jobs.'

Roy knew that she was being perfectly reasonable, a fact that ironically only made him all the more angry. Fortunately Dr Wiles arrived with the medical team to do a full medical examination and was full of such optimism at Roy's most recent breakthrough that his anger slowly abated. He could see and he was reassured that his focus would quickly return to normal. The return of his eyesight augured well for the future but Roy doggedly refused to believe that everything else would come back, without scars. He was sure that he would be permanently disabled in some way and felt mildly uneasy at the optimism of the nurses, sure that they were keeping something from him, and girding himself to cope with the blow when it came.

At last, he was able to be part of the outside world again. Even being able to look out at the window made him feel more connected with the teeming life below and he enjoyed being able to watch the frenetic activity of the ward. Having been deprived of sight for so long, he absorbed all the visual impressions greedily, much as the starving prisoner voraciously wolfs down his first meal without thought as to what he is eating.

Roy's newly returned ability to see was not without problems. Caroline, drawn and pale from the heavy demands placed on her time and energy, was under considerable pressure from the medical staff to start taking it easy.

'Now that Roy has seen what time you have been coming in,

we really think you do not need to arrive until midday. You'll have far more to give to Roy if you're not dropping with exhaustion,' the sister said firmly. 'Don't worry about Roy, we'll have to talk to him,' she said with a glint in her eye.

Even though Roy seemed to do nothing but find fault with the nurses, they were experienced enough to know that he could not always help his actions. As far as Caroline was concerned, the nurses and especially the sisters were a continual source of strength and support.

An interesting change was that prior to his illness, Roy had been shortsighted but now was longsighted and his old glasses were no longer of any use to him. No one seemed to explain why this should be the case. Roy was making medical history and it was difficult for any further predictions to be made with complete certainty.

One of the most unpleasant experiences that Roy had to undergo from time to time was electroconvulsive therapy. Roy used to dread the appearance of the man who administered this treatment, particularly when he tried to convince him that it wouldn't hurt. By giving the patient a series of electric shocks one is able to judge the convulsive response, thereby gaining knowledge of any progress that was being made by the muscles. Had he been able to scream, Roy would have opened his mouth and yelled, so painful were those sessions, but instead had to lie stoically and bear it all.

With the opening of his eyes came the start of facial movements, much to the relief of Caroline. At times she found it so depressing and off putting to explain things to a deadpan face and missed the wide variety of expressions at Roy's disposal and which so epitomised his lively personality.

Physiotherapy was obviously of great importance to Roy's recovery and it now took on a new intensity. It was to be four months before positive improvement began to show. During that period of time physiotherapy consisted of exercising Roy's legs and arms with as much support as he could muster. All of his joints were moved in order that he did not stiffen up completely. When he had gathered too much phlegm in his lungs they would massage his chest to loosen it and enable it to be suctioned out. At times this was an excruciating procedure, in fact, it felt as though the full weight of their body was crushing his rib cage.

During the time that Roy had been lying in bed the physiotherapists had become very worried that when Roy did recover, his feet might have dropped, so they made him wear leg splints for some of the time. At a later date, they were also worried that his hands would turn in on themselves as they had been inactive for such a long time and splints were also made for his hands. The leg splints were bearable but the hand ones would dig into his skin forming red welts on the back of his knuckles.

'I'm sorry but they have to be firm,' the physio insisted, loath to tell him that they were in fact going to be extremely painful after a while. In order to hold the feet and hands firmly in place, the straps had to be pulled very tight over skeleton-like bones which had long ago lost any flesh which could have been used as a barrier.

It was a permanent struggle to strike the right balance between giving him all the benefits of modern technology in what was a very serious illness, and keeping things as simple and normal as possible. Making sure that Roy did not feel anxious or fearful was likely to have as positive an influence on the course of the illness as any medical procedure.

The strain of being permanently strong and in control was beginning to exert its toll on Caroline, who longed to have someone to discuss things with, to voice her innermost fears. Her mother was wonderful but too old, Alex was wonderful but too young . . . Although she had noticed her son grow up overnight, taking his responsibilities as head of the household seriously, she was not prepared to burden him any further with her anxieties. That left the medical staff or Saul. They were both being as supportive as possible. The best way of coping she had found in the long term was not to think negatively. If she let her imagination run away with her she was lost, she would not be able to cope. Her strength in coping was to live on one level only, the level of survival.

Roy was making positive progress, but still completely reliant on his ventilator. One night Caroline had left after giving Roy his goodnight kiss, and he was looking forward to an uneventful night. All of a sudden he became aware that he was unable to breathe properly. Something was wrong with the ventilator, of that he was sure, and he summoned up his pitiful strength to attract the attention of the nurse. She came and laboriously teased out what was wrong.

'Nonsense Roy,' she said briskly, straightening his pillow and sheets and making for the door. 'The ventilator was checked earlier this evening and is in perfectly good order.'

Roy fumed. *Why do those nurses always straighten my sheets, as if doing something excuses them from listening to my real requests. I could die from lack of oxygen but my bed would look tidy . . .*

He tried again, and met with a similar lack of success. Now he was growing desperate and the old panic welled up inside.

I can't breathe properly and Caroline isn't even here to do something.

Each breath seemed to become more shallow and laboured and his growing tension must have caused his lungs to constrict which further reduced what precious air he was getting.

The nurses came to turn him and he tried a final time. One of them glanced vaguely at the ventilator but could see nothing out of the ordinary.

'You're only making it difficult by your anxiety,' she said kindly. 'Try to relax and the breathing will become easier.'

He tried. It didn't.

His longing for sleep had long gone and he knew that he dared not drift off as he might never regain consciousness. He hadn't even said goodbye to Caroline or the children. Perhaps he could get the nurses to call the doctor on duty who might check the ventilator again?

It was a slim hope, unlikely to be realised but enough to keep him going until the next visit from the nurse. She was becoming increasingly exasperated but recognised that his distress was real.

'I'll try and contact the doctor,' she promised. 'He's the only one who can check it.'

Oh, just please get the doctor, he groaned inwardly and lay still, taut, terrified that he would pass out through lack of oxygen.

It seemed like an age before the doctor arrived and examined both Roy and the ventilator.

'I've reassured him that the machine is working fine but he's got himself worked up into a state,' the nurse was saying.

Roy ignored her, too terrified to even feel angry at her dismissal of his concerns. The doctor was a stranger to Roy but reassuring and respectful. He did a thorough examination and found that there was indeed a problem with the ventilator, such that the oxygen level was short.

It was small comfort to be proved right at this stage, especially as it took quite a while to rectify the problem. By the time Roy was at last settled comfortably, breathing easily again and relatively relaxed, it was early morning.

Has no one told them that I've been awake all night, he wondered in irritated bemusement as they appeared to give him his bedwash. *I was just about to go to sleep.* It was pointless, and he was forced to go through the usual routine. When Caroline arrived, she received the usual brunt edge of this distress and complained on his behalf to the ward sister.

'They've promised it won't happen again,' she said, 'the nurse who was looking after Roy is very apologetic.' What else could she say?

Sulking, upset and more loath than ever to let Caroline leave him for even a minute, Roy clung on, desperately trying to attain a semblance of order and control in a world where he was no longer able to influence the actions directly; being blown wherever the fates decreed, helpless and vulnerable and unable any more to act out of free choice and volition.

Chapter Six

MORAL SUPPORT

THE SPEECH therapist taught him how to mouth, placing a spoon or tip of a cotton-wool bud that had been placed in ice onto his tongue in order to stimulate movement. She made him do a range of exercises to get the jaw and whole mouth moving, activities that weren't painful in the way that physiotherapy was, but made him feel such a fool.

Slowly the muscles around his mouth returned and he was aware of an increasing amount of movement which enabled him to mouth his words. Initially, the children were more adept at guessing what he was trying to say, particularly Naomi, who spent every day lip-reading. She was quite often used as the interpreter when everyone had given up trying to decipher what he was trying to say.

There were several Irish nurses on the ward and Roy grew friendly with them all, liking their bright humour and sensitivity to his ever-changing moods. One of them couldn't understand a word of what he was trying to convey and, in despair he tried again, mouthing it this time in a stage-Irish accent. To his surprise and amusement, she understood the message immediately. From then on, Roy's motivation to mouth his words increased markedly, enjoying as he did the games with the various accents with gratifying success.

Another little Irish nurse with straight hair and horn-rimmed glasses had a special soft spot for Roy: it seemed that they both shared the same sense of humour. She was an absent-minded soul but in Roy's moments of despair when he was lying in his bed depressed beyond belief, she would bend down and whisper in his ear, 'Have faith and trust in God Roy.' It was at moments like this that Roy knew he was not alone and this gentle voice somehow gave him renewed faith.

For the first time he also became aware of other patients on the ward. Caroline had been his main link with these kindred spirits, and she used to meet the relatives in the kitchen or in the waiting room, comparing notes or simply offering comfort and support. Now Roy was able to participate in their own private dramas himself, no longer able to cut them completely out of his consciousness.

One man, John, had Guillain-Barre Syndrome. He had suddenly collapsed on his kitchen floor and when his wife discovered him he had stopped breathing. She had to give him artificial respiration – quite a chilling thought – whilst her mother rang for an ambulance. Like Roy, he lay there paralysed and on a ventilator, another entrapped human soul who hung with tenuous links onto the real world. Caroline grew friendly with his wife, the two of them making a formidable team to confront the nurses should the treatment of their husbands not be entirely to their satisfaction. They even maintained contact for a while after her husband had been transferred to another hospital before losing touch. Once back in the mainstream of life and away from the unreal world of the hospital such friendships were hard to maintain without continuing contact and a shared sense of purpose.

There was a certain jealous competitiveness amongst patients who enviously compared their speeds of recovery. At the time, neither Roy nor John could move, let alone communicate, and they remained distant both physically and emotionally from each other.

There was also a fourteen-year-old boy, who by his age alone won sympathy and heartfelt warmth for his tragic predicament. A keen sportsman and just about to do his GCSE's he had contracted a virus which rendered him paralysed from the neck downwards. He was likely to remain paralysed for the rest of his life and on a ventilator, but possessed a cheerful courage that strengthened them all. Without saying much on account of his shyness, he was wheeled around the ward to greet the other patients, including Roy. Alex struck up quite a friendship with him, both sharing a common love of football. Understandably, his parents were distraught and there were long discussions on the ward as to the best school for him to attend. It did help Roy in particular, every time he felt sorry for himself and despaired of ever recovering.

Amongst Roy's visitors were his colleagues from the office. Eric, his partner, came in every week religiously, devastated by Roy's illness and prone to tears when alone with Caroline. He kept Roy informed of the main issues in the office and quickly reassured him that business had never been better. It was the start of the property boom of 1987 and there was no fear that the firm would collapse without Roy's presence. Indeed, none of the estate agencies were in danger of collapsing, according to Eric.

'I can't believe it, Roy,' he told him cheerfully. 'The prices have shot up beyond our wildest dreams and we have more business than we can cope with. You picked a perfect time to have your, er . . . little break.'

Roy was relieved not to have to face a bankrupt firm when he returned but slightly jealous at not being part of this new prosperity and excitement. His initial worries that they would not survive without him became quickly transformed into the concern that they would survive too well.

What if I lose my position, my status within the business, if they feel that they can do without me, he wondered moodily. *What if some of the more ambitious junior partners use this as an opportunity to move upwards in the business and are unable to let me back without resentment, without resistance?*

He supposed that it was arrogance on his part to think that he was indispensable, that the business would not flourish in his absence. Yet, it was his own creation and alongside Eric, he had poured all of his energy into building it up to where it was today. Surely his pride in his achievement was not misplaced, his feelings of indispensability not unfounded?

At least he didn't have to worry about finances. Eric regularly called on Caroline to see if she needed any money and if the hospital bills were covered by the NHS. No private insurance company would pay for the treatment and expensive equipment and Roy reflected ironically on the years of paying private insurance. In the early days Caroline had asked the doctors if Roy would have any better medical attention if he were to attend the hospital privately, not for one moment realising how long Roy's illness was going to take. The doctors' response was that when one is as seriously ill as Roy is and especially as he had such a rare disease, the only place to be was in the NHS. They had at their fingertips the medical brains of the world.

Later when his vision had improved sufficiently to allow him to read, Eric started to bring in the *Estates Gazette*, a professional magazine that helped Roy to keep in touch with the value of property, rocketing up as it was. If he found an article of particular interest he would mark it for the attention of his colleagues and send it to the office.

Not that he had much time for reading in the hospital, given the steady stream of visitors, including regular visits from the rabbi and other members of the community as well as his close personal group of friends. On days when he was too exhausted, Caroline kept the visitors to a minimum, standing guard at the entrance of his room like a protective mother shielding her young. Sometimes, they preferred to be alone, just the two of them, without the effort of having to entertain visitors.

On one such day Roy was sitting up in bed and Caroline was gently stroking his leg under the sheet. 'Oh that's lovely,' he said. 'It's so soothing, don't stop.' He looked at her with love in his eyes – it was one of those magic moments that they seemed to have left far behind. Despite the fact that they were in a public place, they felt alone . . . or were they?

'Hello, I'm the local visiting reverend from Dollis Hill Synagogue,' he said.

Caroline very swiftly removed her hand from under the sheet and with great difficulty tried to keep a straight face . . .

From the start, Roy's alimentary system had seized up and he couldn't eat anything. The paralysis involved his face, mouth, jaw, lips and throat. Nothing functioned and food ceased to have any importance for him, his previous healthy enjoyment in a good meal a thing of the past and having an appetite a distant pleasant memory of life gone by. Instead, he was left with an awful drab monotony, the intense stimulation that a succulent meal could offer no longer available to him, the tantalising odour of a freshly made cup of coffee or newly baked bread unable to penetrate through his paralysed senses.

Alarmed at his increasing weight loss by mid-November, and realising that his stomach was not absorbing anything, a complex procedure of feeding Roy came into being. A nasogastric tube was inserted through the nose and into the stomach which was an extremely uncomfortable process and made Roy gag. Once in place the discomfort did go but most of the food put down that tube had to be suctioned out again because his stomach could not absorb even small amounts. It was soon obvious that Roy was going to need additional feeding of some kind and the doctors finally decided on a special fluid feeding method, in which the fluid was infused through a large vein and the drip line inserted under anaesthetic. The food was a solution of 2,500 calories per day, yellow white in colour and jokingly nicknamed 'soup of the day' by Roy and the children.

It kept him alive, but only just. Moreover, the feed line would become infected regularly and had to be changed. Every day, the doctors would appear, armed with their stethoscopes to listen hopefully to his alimentary canal.

'Any gurgle would be music to my ears,' Dr Wiles joked as yet again there was no sign of the slightest activity.

Indeed, they had to wait until the beginning of December for the first indication that his digestive system had started to function. Roy had been complaining of stomach pains during the night which turned out to be a severe case of constipation. He had to be assisted manually and this led to chronic diarrohea for the next 36 hours. It was like the last straw that broke the camel's back and Roy fell into a deep depression, unable to bear the final indignity that the illness chose to inflict on him.

Am I ever going to be able to lead a normal life, he wondered in despair? *I'm so tired of this constant preoccupation with every single function of my body's system, functions that I was previously unaware of and scarcely knew existed.*

With no sound issuing forth from the lower regions, Dr Wiles sought a second opinion from an eminent specialist. Roy's depression temporarily evaporated as he saw the famous consultant approach his bed. The specialist ordered a full medical examination which lasted for over two hours, during which they took his blood and measured his blood pressure at frequent intervals whilst he was tilted to an upright position and put back lying down again. They also asked simple mathematical questions to see whether his autonomic nervous system, which controls blood pressure among other things, was working and compensating for the changes in position.

'We just want to see how your mental processes are functioning when you're at this angle on the tilt table,' the doctor explained.

There's nothing wrong with my mental processes; it's my body not my mind that's ill, thank you, he thought to himself.

He did, however, appreciate the courtesy and kindness shown to him by the doctors. For all their patronising air in certain matters, they were respectful of his needs and sensitive when he was in such pain and discomfort, responding quickly and efficiently in most cases.

Once the specialist was satisfied that there was sufficient improvement, he prescribed the drug Distigmine to stimulate the internal system. Around this time, Roy 'tasted' his first 'food' which did not need to be suctioned out, fed through the nasogastric tube. Hardly on par with *cordon bleu* cuisine but a hopeful beginning all the same. He longed for the day when he could eat a proper meal yet hated the slow haul towards regaining control over his digestive system more than perhaps any other process. It was incredibly humiliating as he became incontinent and could not yet control his bowels. Caroline came in armed with clean sets of pyjamas each day and comforted him with the fact that he would soon be eating normally.

Still passing urine by means of the catheter, this frequently became infected and he was given bladder wash outs twice daily. These were agonisingly painful but he gritted his teeth in determination, concentrating on what they were doing to provide another focus to the pain. The nurses first clamped off the catheter and introduced the saline solution into his bladder. It was at that stage that he experienced the shooting pain and an intolerable burning sensation in his penis and bladder.

Nor did this procedure always work and infections still occurred. In such instances, the catheter was removed completely and he was put on antibiotics . . . with all the usual painful complications of collapsed veins and the tortuous search for new sites. Reinserting the catheter was but another chapter in the book of uncomfortable procedures and usually done under a local anaesthetic. Upon one such occasion, the doctor putting ice packs around his groin wittily remarked.

'Roy, this must be the first bit of excitement you've had down there for months.'

Needless to say, the surrounding staff collapsed into laughter and Roy himself was greatly amused, glad to have something to divert him from an unpleasant event. It wasn't until towards the end of December that he was at last able to pass water naturally and get rid of that contraption, a source of constant pain and great indignity. From then on, he urinated into a bottle and the amount of urine was measured daily.

The course of recovery did not run smoothly and Roy was easily disheartened by each setback. Just before Christmas a number of visitors and nurses commented on Roy's colour and expressed surprise that his tan had lasted for so long after his holiday during the summer. It appeared that Roy had developed jaundice and would have to be transferred unexpectedly to St Thomas's Hospital because they needed access to a liver-scanning machine.

When Caroline told him that morning he was horrified, as she knew he would be. She herself had only heard the news an hour or so earlier as it had been a fairly quick decision of the doctors.

'Only for a while and then you'll be coming back here,' she reassured him, her voice lacking conviction.

They were both getting too tired to be uprooted again and Queen Square had become like a second home, safe and comfortably familiar. As if the move wasn't disturbing enough, she had been told that they might have to operate on Roy for gallstones. The idea of operating on him in his present weak state terrified her beyond belief, and she decided to withhold that information from Roy until it became a certainty.

I can't believe that such an important hospital doesn't have a liver-scanning machine, he communicated to Caroline, who merely shrugged her shoulders helplessly.

She had been through it already with the doctors and was told that there was no alternative. St Thomas's seemed to be the natural choice because Dr Wiles was also a consultant there and most of the medical team that he worked with there were already familiar with Roy's case.

'We can't afford to take the risk,' Dr Wiles informed her. 'If the jaundice gets worse it could pose a very serious problem, given that he is so weak and lacking in any resistance.'

Fortunately the drive was easy and Roy was accompanied by the ward sister, an anaesthetist and the portable ventilator. Upon his arrival he was taken up to the Intensive Care and subjected to a range of tests, including respiratory and blood monitoring. Imagine his excitement when they discovered that he had been getting too much oxygen.

'This can have an inhibiting effect on breathing,' the doctor told Roy and Caroline who listened in amazement. He was older than any of their doctors so far but bore the look of an experienced physician who was guided as much by his intuition as by the volumes of medical texts. It had been that intuition that caused the two doctors who were looking after Roy to check the levels of oxygen and would explain why Roy was making so little progress in trying to breath for himself. Ironically, the whole transfer turned out to be a storm in a tea cup – he returned to Queen Square three days later. During this time there was sufficient improvement in his jaundice and the operation was deemed unnecessary.

In spite of the disruption, they were grateful to the doctors at St Thomas's for their readjustment of the oxygen level and Roy started to make rapid progress in this direction. None the less, his return to Queen Square was marred by the fact that his old position on the ward had been taken.

Chapter Seven

FIFTIETH BIRTHDAY PARTY

'HE'S ONLY been gone for three days,' Caroline exclaimed, looking at the sister in disbelief. 'Surely you could have put the new patient somewhere else; it's not as if the ward is full.'

'We could have but we didn't know how long Roy was going to be away,' the sister replied firmly, 'and we needed that bed which is reserved for those patients demanding almost twenty-four-hour monitoring. Roy is no longer so sick and could manage just as well in another spot on the ward.'

'But you know he hates disruption,' Caroline cried. 'He was so comfortable in his little niche and is very upset at the prospect of settling somewhere else.'

'Exactly, which is another reason why we moved him.'

Caroline glanced sharply at the sister, only to be met with the steadfast gaze of two compassionate but firm blue eyes. With dawning realisation, Caroline looked up slowly. 'Oh . . . I see,' she said falteringly.

She suddenly understood that the move was part of their policy to discourage institutionalisation, a trap into which Roy had clearly fallen. He now feared and hated change so much that even the slightest disruption to his routine upset him tremendously. Indeed, he no longer spoke much of returning home and she understood that there were going to be many hurdles to overcome aside from the purely medical ones.

Christmas was now on top of them almost before they realised it. Although not a big festival amongst the Jewish community, they couldn't help but be affected by the excitement and build up around them – coloured lights and decorations on the street and in the shops, advertisements from those in the entertainment business, parties. It was a time of the year that Roy had loved, enjoying the contrast between the warmth of the festivities and the cold crispness of the winter season. As he lay moodily in his bed, he gradually appreciated how much he missed the children, particularly at this time of the year. He was going to miss his end-of-year break and the high spirits in the office that went with it. Even the nurses on the ward were rushing around with smiles on their faces, chatting excitedly about going home for the holiday. Roy's gloom deepened and was accentuated by a growing panic at the prospect of the replacements for the routine nurses. Most of the regular staff were taking a few days' leave and he dreaded trying to explain to the new nurses what he needed and how they could make him comfortable. In fact, he was feeling very sorry for himself.

'Nonsense, Roy,' Caroline eventually said in exasperation. 'It will be fine, I'm sure. The new nurses will have received explicit instructions as to what you need and I'll be here. The children will also be able to see more of you, so don't worry.'

His gloom deepened as he added guilt to his range of negative emotions. It wasn't fair to ask the children to have all their holidays in hospital and yet, how else were they going to be able to share Caroline?

The nurses set up a Christmas fund to finance a party for the team in Intensive Care and, as a result, enormous amounts of food were brought in. Roy and Caroline added food hampers for the nurses and a bottle of whisky or brandy for the doctors. It was the best way they could think of conveying their gratitude for the wonderful medical care given to Roy so far and their gifts seemed to be a great success. Some of the more unusual delicacies from the hampers were even hidden from thieving nurses from other wards.

Christmas Day itself was far better than any of them had anticipated and even Roy rather enjoyed it. One doctor dressed up as Father Christmas, posed by his bed with the senior sister for a photograph. Roy even tried a little wine; one sip was enough to tell him that he was in no way ready for it, he found it bitter and acid, quite different to what he had expected. It was the only mar to the day and he suddenly had the first uneasy hint that eating and drinking was perhaps not going to bring the instant pure pleasure that he had dreamt about.

Roy was especially pleased to see his brother Basil, over from South Africa with his wife on their habitual annual visit. True to their promise to Caroline, his brothers had restrained themselves from rushing over to London the minute they heard how seriously ill Roy was, but they kept in close contact by phone calls and letters. Now, looking down at his younger brother lying so helplessly in bed, Basil was deeply shocked and had to muster all his self-control to prevent his expression from betraying his upset. Roy was not fooled but found his presence reassuring, knowing that he was due to come anyway and so not reading anything untoward into the visit.

Basil spent much of the time by the bedside, relieving Caroline and allowing her some time to herself. He did much to lift both of their spirits, reminiscing about happier times and joking with Roy and Caroline. During that period, Roy had yet another of his setbacks, having incurred another infection which was subsequently diagnosed as septicaemia. Again, he had little choice but to go on a course of antibiotics and Basil sat with him all day until the temperature subsided. Caroline was deeply touched, desperately drawing on the comfort he offered and feeling for the first time that she was able to share the burden. Although a friend visited Roy every Friday night to recite *Kiddush*, it was not the same intimate support that could only come from another member of the family. They both missed Basil terribly when he had to return but felt strengthened by his visit, ready to battle afresh with whatever the New Year might bring.

The New Year brought with it new hope, and for the first time Roy stopped taking one step forward and two backwards. The improvements seemed to be real and lasting and he embarked in earnest on the road to health. Perhaps the use of the word 'earnest' was a little premature at that stage, for he was more intent on maintaining the status quo than on breaking any notable records. Everything was such an effort and he began to dread the enthusiasm of the medical staff as they introduced what he saw as yet another tortuous procedure to help him regain control over his awakening body.

As a result, he greeted those early sessions on the tilt table with open antagonism. All Roy wanted was to lie in peace, and the stepping-up of the physiotherapy did nothing to contribute towards his immediate comfort. On the contrary, each movement was difficult and exhausting and he had to be goaded and cajoled every inch of the way.

Not that recovery didn't bring its share of problems. As he became more used to being in a vertical position, he was made to sit in a chair, at first for a few minutes and then gradually for longer periods. Having spent months just lying on his back, a whole new vista suddenly opened up for Roy. He sat upright for the first time and gazed around with a new wonder. Then he looked down at his body and was devastated. His legs! Previously proud of his physique – the firm muscles of his thighs and absence of an inch of flab anywhere – he now realised the extent of the disintegration. The term 'thigh' hardly did justice to those wasted members, those matchsticks with the skin falling in loose folds over his bones, once covered in flesh but now jutting out in an obscene gesture. He was uncomfortably reminded of famine victims in Third World countries such as Ethiopia, whom he had recently observed sympathetically in the news.

The ghastly reality of the illness pierced his consciousness with a harsh brutality, battering at his self-respect and self-confidence. No one must see him like this. His vanity and sense of manhood were deeply offended but the effect went much deeper than that. Given the extent of the damage, Roy became convinced that he could never possibly recover . . . not completely anyway. Something wasn't going to come back. He grew worried that he would be in a wheelchair for ages – perhaps for ever – and the prospect terrified him. In fact, to Roy, life wouldn't be worth living as a cripple. It was one thing to survive such an illness but on what level? They kept putting the splints on his hands and feet, worrying him with their concerns. Was he ever going to walk again, not to mind about dragged feet? Would he ever speak? How could he function in the office if he couldn't even lift a telephone?

With the weight loss had come a total weakness and the effort of standing so exhausted him that he would collapse afterwards on the bed, unwilling to try for longer than was absolutely necessary. It was like being a baby, basic functions that he'd taken for granted had to be relearned all over again from scratch. Bitter tears of frustration characterised those early physiotherapy sessions and he grew more depressed and irritable than ever.

Caroline strove to uphold his morale and provide him with the necessary motivation to work at getting better. She had been warned

again and again by the medical staff of the dangers if Roy gave
himself up to apathy and lethargy, and was determined that he
would continue to fight, having come this far already.

'You can't shut everyone out until you feel less self-conscious –
it's going to take weeks, even months before you look like your old
self again.'

Is that supposed to comfort me, he wondered gloomily?

'How you look is not the main thing,' she continued. 'It's you
we care about, not what your body looks like.'

Funny, isn't it, he mused, as she left him to think over her words.
*This whole illness has really brought into question who I am. I always
identified strongly with my body – how I look, how fit I am, how I feel
physically. Since I've been ill, that has no longer been possible and yet I'm
still very much here, I'm still alive. Who are we really? What is it that
makes us human, that gives us our identity?*

Amidst endless reassurance, Roy gradually came to terms with
his sense of looking like a freak and allowed certain visitors still to
come and see him. He was now more than ready to suffer whatever
humiliations came in the slow process towards regaining control of
his digestive and eliminative functions, knowing that this was the
first stage towards rebuilding his body.

The push to get his digestive system back to normal had taken
on a new intensity. One of the doctors in charge of the treatment
came to examine Roy just before going on holiday in late January.

'You should be able to start on puréed food now,' he advised.
'Try a few soups before I come back and see how you get along.'

Caroline decided to make them at home, knowing how lacking
in nutrition most hospital food was. She cleared with the doctor
what food he could try, and asked him when he would be back.

'I'm just going for two weeks. And one thing's for sure, I won't
be eating anything on the plane, Roy,' he added laughing.

Roy smiled, at last able to move his facial muscles ever so slightly.
He too had resolved never to eat on planes, trains or boats ever
again in his life. That is, if he ever made it on a plane again. Even
restaurants were looking extremely improbable at that moment.

Caroline started to bring in puréed soups and he awaited them
in the beginning with eagerness, knowing of old his passion for
such wholesome food. Then, his fantasies over what he would eat
that day quickly collapsed into profound disappointment. Everything was completely flavourless. It was the ultimate disappointment

to weeks of hard work and discomfort as they all struggled to get his digestive system working normally.

'It's to be expected,' Dr Wiles reassured him. 'You've been on some fairly potent medication and one of its unfortunate side effects can be to destroy the taste buds. Don't worry, they will return to normal in time.'

Roy hoped that he was right. So bland and dull did the soup taste that his interest in food was short-lived. Although his gastrointestinal system was showing signs of awakening, he was still getting most of his meals on nasogastric tube feeding. He had come to hate those yellow food bags that were rigged up to the drip. Whenever he was given such a feed he felt nauseous and tended to blame the 'Food'. It felt just like a bilious attack and the liquid frequently had to be suctioned out again. All in all, life was one dreary struggle as far as Roy was concerned, and he could see little to look forward to.

Then out of the blue some of his prayers were partially answered and an unforeseen event gave him the necessary push to snap out of his depression. It was a Sunday evening and he had just rejected Caroline's homemade puréed soup, disappointed and depressed that each meal fell so far short of expectations. It was at that moment that the ward became alive with excitement as they prepared for the latest admission – the Marquis of Tavistock. Diagnosed with a massive stroke, caused by an aneurism, he was initially given a private room in the isolation unit as he was so unwell, indeed there were doubts as to whether he was going to survive. He had an emergency operation and was later moved to Intensive Care, much to the delight of all. Roy was particularly interested to discover that the marquis was the freeholder for the Bedford Estates and was thus the grand landlord for the National Hospital itself.

The telephone started to ring – the Prime Minister, the Queen, the Archbishop of Canterbury. Roy's ears burned and for the first time, he forgot about his own miseries in his eagerness to follow what was going on around him. The growing fervour increased over the next few days as they were graced by a steady stream of illustrious visitors. It certainly rated high on entertainment value, and if Roy had needed any motivation to persevere with his physio-therapy, he needed none now. At last he had something worth sitting up for as he gaped in amazement at hampers coming in from Harrods and ice-cream from Claridges, not to mention the marquis's private butler who cooked tasty little morsels on the ward. It was when he made the most wonderful cheese soufflé that Roy's mouth really began to water and he actually desired to eat for the first time. Fortunately, Caroline was more amused than put out when she arrived with his soup, only to discover that he had been offered and accepted half of the marquis's lunch. Sadly, even that had tasted somewhat strange and it was only much later that his taste buds returned completely to normal.

Almost overnight, he became more mobile. No longer did the physiotherapists have to cajole and nag him to take those few extra steps, and his attention was always drawn to the excitement that was going on outside. He would persuade Caroline or a nurse to take him out into the corridor so that he could see all of the personalities coming in – the American ambassador, David Jacobs . . . Then it was his own turn, and with head held proudly high, he would walk slowly up and down the corridor with his frame, showing them how much he had improved. They encouraged him by telling him how well he was doing and he strutted like a peacock, enjoying the attention immensely.

The three sons of the marquis were regular visitors, along with their mother. While the marquis was ill, the running of the estate fell on the shoulders of his wife and their staff and she managed to cope with what really was a very large enterprise. The eldest boy would often sit up all night with his father. Having recovered from a near fatal accident himself, he was now able to return his father's own devotion and Roy and Caroline were pleased to observe such a close-knit family in those circles. The marchioness was a delightful woman and Roy could recall reading about their wedding many years ago in the gossip column. She had been a beautiful debutante and was still an extremely attractive woman and charming along with it.

On the afternoon of the race the entire ward was in particularly high spirits. The marquis owned a racehorse which had been entered for the three o'clock at Exeter. His sons had placed bets, persuading even the nurses to back their horse, and patients and nurses alike were glued to the television to watch the race. As the leading horse approached the finishing line, their horse suddenly surged to the front and came in a close second. The quiet sanctity of the Intensive Care was rudely disturbed by the excited eruptions from all. Although not a racing man himself, Roy joined in the fun with hearty enjoyment. It did them all good, although the wrath of Sister

Dillon who was absent from this raucous scene, would have most likely fallen on the merry scene.

Roy was sorry not to have been able to talk to the marquis himself, but his illness had been severe and it took much longer before he could speak. However, his presence was deeply felt and his influence seemed to stretch far and wide. Stepping up with his physiotherapy with slightly less resentment – bouncing on a rubber ball, walking with a frame, chest exercise – Roy was now gaining in strength every day. Instead of having physiotherapy on the ward, he now had to go down to the physiotherapy department in his wheelchair.

Then Caroline announced gaily that they were going to have a birthday party! Roy gaped at her in horror, thinking that either she was going mad or else was making a joke in very poor taste. Neither was the case and she informed him that he was celebrating his fiftieth birthday in style . . . on the ward. It was the last thing he wanted, and felt in no shape, physically or mentally, to enjoy a party. He dreaded in particular too many people seeing him in his present condition. Each day was so different that he never knew whether he would feel up to being sociable.

Roy became angry with Caroline. After all, hadn't he told her well before his illness that he didn't intend having a party on his fiftieth birthday? Now, lying in hospital, helpless and looking like a Biafran, he certainly wasn't in the humour for entertaining.

Unfortunately, she wasn't to be dissuaded.

'We need to keep having goals for ourselves or else we'll go mad,' she told him bluntly after he lodged his strong objections as best as he could. 'Particularly the children . . . they needed something to aim for, to plan and organise with my help. All you have to do is attend.'

Caroline had no social life during his illness and this was an ideal opportunity to see some of their friends and to thank them warmly for all of their support. Needless to say, none of this was uppermost in Roy's mind at the time, and he voiced all of his objections, repeatedly, vociferously to deaf ears. Caroline's mother beavered away at home to make all the food and the hospital produced a birthday cake with candles. Roy was torn between admiration for his wife's willpower and exasperation at what he regarded as an immense waste of time. The nurses had been very understanding and felt that the party would give him a boost.

'Because it's at the weekend which is usually a quiet time, we're going to clear the isolation room so that you can meet there. It will give you some privacy and avoid disturbing the other patients,' the sister told Roy one morning expecting him to feel grateful that the medical staff were being so accommodating.

Do they not realise how much I'm dreading the event? Why can't they put an end to the plans by saying that a party would be too disruptive . . . anything really so that I don't have to go through the ordeal?

On 23 January, attached to a portable ventilator, Roy was wheeled grandly into the adjoining room where his family and about a dozen friends were gathered. Rachel had prepared a tape of his favourite music which she put on just as he entered the room. Roy looked extremely touched by this gesture and Caroline congratulated inwardly whichever of the children it had been who came up with that brainwave. At least some of the impatience and air of being there under sufferance had dissolved, although he still looked tense and uncomfortable.

The children were very excited at the prospect of a party and were on their best behaviour handing around sandwiches, cakes, biscuits and tea which the guests tucked into with obvious enjoyment. Their high-spirits were infectious and even Roy found himself occasionally forgetting his increasing discomfort in the festive mood.

A photograph was taken of Roy and another patient, both with nasal gastric tubes and Roy in his wheelchair attached to a portable ventilator. They looked quite a sight!

In spite of all his grumblings, he did enjoy it. However, it was predictably exhausting, and his bottom ached from sitting on a chair for two hours. Unable to speak, he had to make a superhuman effort to mouth his words, with Naomi acting as valiant interpreter. He still couldn't eat solids but managed to sip a mouthful of tea. It was with relief that he finally bade guests goodbye after the obligatory two hours was up. He escaped gratefully to his bed, glad that none of them had overstayed their welcome and worn him out completely.

Caroline watched the bent figure hobbling down the corridor. She could barely recognise the husband who, several months ago, had engineered outing after outing in the South of France. He now looked like a wizened old man, thin, frail, uncertain on his feet.

Nonetheless, the radiant expression on his face as he finally made it to where she was standing reminded her once again of the old Roy, the man she knew and loved and not the cantankerous patient who drained her of all her strength and time. It was an expression of triumph, of a goal hard-fought for being finally achieved, conquered.

'I made it,' he mouthed, and she didn't have any problem interpreting that sentence.

Roy gave a broad smile. It felt wonderful to be moving towards walking on his own. He had gone from a wheelchair, graduating onto the parallel bars in the gym until finally he had been able to balance himself on a stick. At the same time, the painful stomach injections to prevent his blood from clotting were at last dropped. Now that he was taking exercise, such injections were no longer necessary.

Chapter Eight

THE LONG HAUL BACK TO HEALTH

THE SIMPLEST of movements that he had taken completely for granted before his illness now became major obstacles to overcome. He had to push himself from lying, into a sitting position instead of being pulled up by the nurse and found even this simple act incredibly difficult, having lost all strength in his arms. It took many attempts before he even managed this once, whilst standing up from a sitting position seemed to be well nigh impossible. Even his arms wouldn't stretch up farther than shoulder height. Everything had seized up completely and he felt as if he was stepping back into his body after a vacation, during which it had become rather shoddy and secondhand. Roy felt devastated at the amount of damage just lying on a bed could do and daunted at the prospect of working his way back to normality.

As he was managing to stand, the bed baths were stopped and the nurses insisted that he learn to wash himself.

'You're going to have to do it once you go home, so you might as well start now,' the nurses told him and he grew suddenly tense. *Going home?* No one had mentioned that to him. *Was this a new plan hatching, one about which I will be informed at the eleventh hour?*

To his relief, he discovered that he was reading too much into throwaway remarks.

I'm certainly not ready to go home, he decided. *It's an arduous enough task to walk, and it takes so long that I have little strength or mobility to reach all of the difficult parts of my body.*

The nurses refused to help, knowing that unless he did it for himself, he would never learn to stop relying on them. Roy resented their lack of co-operation, especially when he became very tired and felt he couldn't do more.

As if this wasn't enough, he was also re-learning to dress himself. Like washing, it took an interminable age and he couldn't even bend down to his feet; he had to lift one leg over the other in order to get his sock on. This often took so long that he was irritable and worn out by the time he had mastered even one garment. He was given a sort of hook to hoist the vest over his head as he still couldn't raise his arms sufficiently – it was a battle and a struggle every morning.

Why can't they help me, he wondered resentfully, as the nurses watched from afar but refused to step in to intervene.

It was the only way to force Roy to make the effort, to relearn those fundamental movements. Playing cards, draughts and chess – all encouraged him to improve his concentration but it was a full-time job persuading him to do anything, so strong had the inclination to do nothing grown.

By March he had also started Occupational Therapy. The therapists really challenged him to use his limbs and exercise his muscles. Even draughts were played on the wall so as to maximise the stretch and he now mingled more freely with the other patients.

The most difficult step of all was the weaning off the ventilator. Roy had come to rely on it so totally that he had forgotten on one level what life had been like before he lost the ability to breathe on his own. There wasn't a day when he didn't fret as to whether he was getting enough oxygen, for his breathing affected his whole well-being.

After Roy's return from St Thomas's his breathing capacity rose immediately from 50 ml to 300 ml when blowing into a spirometer. To give some sort of idea as to the magnitude of this figure, Roy had been informed that his breathing capacity would need to increase to at least 1,000 ml before he could start being weaned off the machine. Gradually, he built it up from 300 to 400 to 550 ... When he finally hit the 1,000 mark by the second week of February, the doctors decided that he was at last ready to be weaned off, a pronouncement greeted with much terror by all involved. While he was glad that he was showing a steady improvement, he dreaded leaving the safety and comfort of the machine.

The nurses told him that people were usually frightened, especially at night when they feared that they would fall off to sleep without the machine, have difficulty breathing and imagine that they would not wake up again. Needless to say, his terror of the nights increased and he was unable to go to sleep unless reassured that the machine was switched on and working. Although they only withdrew the ventilator for a few minutes at first, he felt as if it was a real struggle to breathe and he returned gratefully to his life support. It had become deeply ingrained in his subconscious that he couldn't do without the machine and he resisted them every step of the way to become independent of it.

By the end of February he had achieved a period of four hours breathing on his own, a very positive indication that his lungs were beginning to strengthen. Once he became used to the idea the nurses pushed him even faster and one day he fell asleep without the ventilator. As he slowly awoke, the awful fact gradually dawned on him and he froze in petrified horror, a feeling of sickness flooding through every pore of his body.

Oh my God, I've been asleep but I'm still here and breathing. Naturally, the nurses had also noticed what was happening and joked with him.

'You've been having us all on,' they all said. 'All this fuss about the ventilator! If we didn't know you better, we might even suspect you of malingering!'

It was just the opportunity that the medical staff needed to take him off the ventilator for most of the day. However, Roy remained adamant that it remained on during the night and agreed to a compromise of having it switched on at midnight. Until then, he lay awake fitfully, too nervous to risk falling asleep again, in spite of perpetual reassurances from the doctors. They subjected him to constant pressure to extend the time off the ventilator but he fought them all the way.

'It's a constant battle of wills,' Dr Wiles told Caroline. 'We must make the final break somehow.' Unbeknown to her the anaesthetist had altered the setting on the ventilator so that Roy was finding it easier to breathe without the ventilator. All the demands that the machine be checked brought no satisfaction and they all told Roy that he was imagining things.

They've definitely fiddled with it and there's nothing I can do about it, he pondered gloomily, angry that they would tamper with what had become the most essential thing to his hospital existence.

With each hour that he managed breathing on his own, Roy's

confidence grew. The climax came one night when he lost his temper with the night nurse, demanding that they turn the ventilator off.

'Of course,' she said quietly, the trace of a smile in her eyes the only betrayal that this was exactly what they had planned.

By reducing the flow of oxygen, Roy was getting more air without the ventilator than with it. It was the perfect strategy to break the psychological dependence without any major confrontation, while at the same time making the transition so gradual as to allow him to build up his strength and ability to breathe alone for long periods of time.

During this period of weaning off the ventilator, the nurses were very careful that someone was watching Roy very closely as they did not want him suddenly to have a relapse, which did in fact happen once, when he developed a fever and had to have the ventilator switched on again for a short period of time.

Now, in the site of the tracheotomy where the ventilator had been the doctor inserted a silver tube to help his speech. Well before this, the medical staff had been anxious to know whether any attempts to talk would be successful and they tested his vocal cords. He had been able to make sounds of a sort but they were not very coherent and Roy found the process uncomfortable. Dr Wiles insisted that the site remain open for several months in case of further complications which might necessitate immediate access to the lungs. Roy agreed, although he did long for the time when he could do away with those endless tubes.

The silver tube at last permitted him to speak, at the beginning of March, but his voice sounded very strange – like a whisper at first and high pitched. Sister told Caroline she was sure Roy was going to have a cockney accent and was quite surprised that his voice was so 'posh'. His voice didn't return back to normal for some three to four months when the tube was finally removed. Another tube, also silver, was inserted at night to allow him to breathe freely but did not enable him to speak. It got quite confusing when the day staff spoke to him as they came in on their early shift, forgetting that he could not reply until they had changed the tubes.

About mid-February Roy had his first taste of fresh air in months. It turned into a family outing, with Caroline, the three children, one nurse, one physiotherapist and the portable ventilator and suction machine in tow. They wrapped him up in blankets, scarfs, his golfing hat and a ski anorak to keep him warm and wheeled him out, objecting violently at the disruption and invasion of his peace.

'Of course you want to go out Daddy,' Rachel interrupted, ignoring the questionable look from her father. 'It's a lovely day and we can show you the flowers in the gardens.'

Caroline smiled in spite of her anxiety. Rachel was sounding more and more like Roy every day and was the only one who seemed to be able to handle him. As for the outing, she was definitely in favour of re-introducing Roy to the 'great outside'. Despite the wintery sunshine, there was a sharp bite to the air and she was worried that he might get cold. Still, the doctor had felt that it would do him good to go out for a short time. It might help to shake him out of his comfortable complacency, to get him used to the idea of change again instead of the constancy and predictability that they had striven to maintain on the ward.

As they set out, the small entourage surrounding a pale figure in a wheelchair muffled up in a hat and thick woollens, people turned around to look more closely. He did appear rather strange and Roy became extremely self-conscious as he saw Queen Square for the first time since his illness. Great Ormond Street Hospital, the Homeopathic Hospital, the old Italian Hospital . . . buildings he had only heard of but not seen were pointed out. Six months later, Roy was now becoming acquainted with the neighbourhood. Down Southampton Row amidst the crowds of staring faces. His embarrassment increased tenfold as the nurse pointed out the local restaurants where friends had gone after visiting him, terrified that he might see someone he knew. It was exciting to be out amidst the noise but it all seemed at one removed, he didn't feel part of it as he couldn't move or join in the bustle. Being pushed around in a wheelchair wasn't exactly what one might have in mind when deciding to take fresh air.

Despite the layers of clothing Roy still felt cold, probably because he had lost so much weight, so on the first occasion the outing was only for about twenty minutes.

He hadn't wanted to go, yet, although drained and ready to collapse on the bed the minute they got back, Roy felt very proud of himself for days after that first outing. The medical staff pushed him firmly from behind, much as a parent lets the child out into increasing freedom, giving the timid one a gentle push while holding the impetuous ones ever so slightly back until they are ready for the challenges that the real world offers.

The outing a few days later was an 'all time first'. Roy's appearance at this stage very closely resembled that of an emaciated, absent-minded professor with long wisps of hair hanging down his neck. He found himself being wheeled into a ladies hairdresser which was just round the corner from the hospital. He had never been in one before for himself and here he felt completely like a fish out of water. However, once he had his hair shampooed and cut he did feel much better and began to enjoy something of the little outing.

The very first signs of spring were making themselves felt and Roy noticed tiny daffodils peeping out, causing him to think of home and their own garden for the first time in ages. He saw the gaping holes where the trees had been blown down in the hurricane and the tiny buds on the ones still left.

So they weren't all blown down after all . . .

The vivid colours of the scene struck him forcibly, even though it was still winter and Roy recognised the beauty in a world that he had previously taken for granted. It was a rich experience and a new awareness.

On his next outing, Alex took over the pushing of his wheelchair and, as if sensing Roy's inner frustration, stepped up the pace somewhat. Their leisurely stroll escalated into a semi-gallop through the hospital gardens until sharply called to a halt by Caroline. Roy knew that he couldn't blame the children for looking for some excitement, so boring had their weekends become as they spent long hours at the hospital. Fortunately, friends had been very good to them, inviting all three out for meals, outings and other pleasant diversions to remove some of the burden from Caroline.

Alex had been a tower of strength during Roy's illness. He went to school in the City so most evenings after school he would pop in to see Roy and give him a progress report of his day's activities. The bond between father and son had always been strong and it was important for both of them to reinforce their interest in and care for each other.

The gentle pushes were getting more insistent, and occupational therapy now really came into its own. Roy played cards to increase finger mobility, progressing after several days to a printing press which he had to set up with the help of a therapist.

'You need to see the project through from start to finish,' she told him while he grumbled that it would be much quicker if she set it up for him.

Within days he acknowledged that she had been right. He had decided to make visiting cards for Caroline, the purpose being to increase his concentration, motivation and attention to detail. Roy had to pick out all the tiny letters one by one and assemble them into lines, and then design the layout and print, an activity that involved pulling vigorously on a lever with his arms. The task really caught his imagination and he was much more willing to make an effort than he had been in doing more, 'mindless' exercises.

'It gives you a first class insight into the laborious procedure used by the printers of old, when everything had to be done by hand,' he told Caroline. She was delighted to see him truly engaged in something outside of himself and his botulism, having feared that he would never regain his old interest in life and his ever-questioning fascination with people and things.

The impetus, however, towards self-sufficiency attracted far less motivated determination and it was a struggle to get Roy to co-operate. With time, he eventually managed to wash and dress himself without assistance and to move from one side to the other in bed without needing to call a nurse. It was slow, tiring and invariably only half done and she was reminded of the children when they first began to dress themselves – jumpers with the buttons done up to leave one short at the bottom, untucked shirts hanging beneath their jumpers, untied shoe laces. Roy would get so frustrated and disheartened with the finished attempt that he would beg the nurses to help him. They refused, knowing that the only way he would build up his dexterity was if they made him do it himself.

It will be much quicker if they help me, Roy grumbled angrily to himself as he struggled to pull on his socks.

As if all that wasn't exhausting enough, first thing in the morning, Roy now was also attending the gym. The physiotherapists were working on improving his mobility and would bring him down in his wheelchair for twice daily exercise. Here he learned how to move on and off the wheelchair by himself, and to raise his body and sit down without assistance. These activities required muscular strength which was extremely limited at that stage, making visits to the gym another drain on his reserves. Roy would fall into a deep sleep when he returned to the ward after such sessions but was awoken after a while so that he would sleep properly at night. Not that he ever got a full night's sleep anyway, what with the niggling interruptions at periodic intervals to give him his medications, monitor his blood pressure and turn him.

Everything had to be relearned from scratch – standing, walking, first with a frame and later with sticks, lifting his arm upwards, balance. He was helpless and had to slowly rebuild his muscle strength, step by step with many setbacks and disappointments along the way.

The last of his supports, the intravenous feeding was the next thing to go and he started on small amounts of solids, taking care to avoid hard foods that he might have difficulty in swallowing. His swallowing reflex was not quite normal but was coming back gradually. This was a long time in coming because it was essential that Roy's swallowing reflex was strong enough to make sure the food went down the oesophagus into the stomach and not into the lungs via the windpipe.

Unfortunately, his taste buds were to take much longer to return to normal and food was one constant disappointment.

I've been looking forward to this moment for months and it's such a let-down, he thought as he gazed gloomily at this half-eaten scrambled egg. *It looks like an egg but that's about as much as I can say; it tastes like goodness only knows what but it isn't egg, of that I'm sure.*

He could see Caroline watching him anxiously, which girded him to pick up his fork and guiltily try another mouthful of the meal she had prepared for him with such care. It tasted so bland and insipid that had he not known what a good cook Caroline was he would have presumed that the fault lay with her.

I wish it did, he grumbled, knowing that it was his failure and not hers. *Everything tastes awful, no matter what, where or with whom I eat.*

Will I ever be able to enjoy my food again?

He was told that he would, but how long would it take? He just had to carry on hoping in the end that everything would work out. Even though Dr Wiles had assured him his taste buds would be restored to normality, at this stage he found it very difficult to believe.

Those last few weeks in the National were geared chiefly towards increasing his self-sufficiency. This had several implications; none of which appealed much to Roy. He had none the less little choice but to accept them.

'We're going to have to toughen him up,' the sister explained tactfully to Caroline. 'Give him far less personal attention and assistance to start with.'

'He won't like that,' Caroline observed judiciously.

'No, he doesn't,' the sister smiled, recalling already a scene from the morning when Roy blew his top because the nurses refused to help him dress. He blamed them for his being late for Physiotherapy, refusing still to take responsibility for getting himself there on time, even if it meant starting to dress a little bit earlier.

'He's going to have to learn to be independent, to plan things so that he can cope, given his disabilities. It's the only way that he will really get better and be able to care for himself. Now, this includes you too; you can't go on being at his beck and call indefinitely, for his sake as much as your own.'

Caroline nodded, knowing that she was right but wondering how it was going to work out in practice. Once again, she was reminded of a child who was refusing to grow up and become more independent. You had to be really strong to resist the temptation just to give in in the face of a full-blown tantrum; doing whatever task was in question was usually far easier than facing the emotional outburst.

'I'm just so tired these days, I don't know if I can face his ill-temper and sulks,' she confessed.

'I know, and we're not asking you to turn your back on him,' the sister reassured her. 'But you know the old cliché – "you have to be cruel to be kind". It's exactly the same here and you must think about it in those terms. You're not helping him by being there all day, doing every little task for him, pandering to him like a spoilt child.'

Caroline agreed, resigned to the repercussions that would inevitably follow her withdrawing slightly from her position in the front line.

They weren't long in coming – Roy did not like it. Indeed, she had to suffer his icy fury for two full days when she announced that she would come in after lunch at the weekends so that she could spend some time with the children. She knew that it was important to prepare him for his transfer to the rehabilitation centre in East Finchley, which was coming up soon, and steeled her resolve so as not to give in.

As part of this preparation, Roy spent his first day at home. To the relief of all, a nurse accompanied him in case there were any problems with his breathing, swallowing or suction, a pleasant Welsh girl with whom he got on well. Accompanied by all his usual gadgets – a ventilator and a portable suction machine – he nervously set off in the late morning. Caroline had prepared the lunch early in the day leaving the chicken in the oven and driven to the hospital to prepare her wounded soldier.

The children were excitedly finishing off a huge banner with the words 'Welcome Home Daddy!' plastered on it. Caroline was feeling nervous. After seven months within the confines of the hospital, what sort of memories would he hold of home? Would his expectations be fulfilled when he returned?

Alex surveyed the scene equally critically from the top of the stairs, having spent the entire morning organising his sisters to do most of the work. He felt the responsibility as man of the household to welcome their guest . . . father . . . as best as they could.

As the ambulance drove up, Roy noticed that Caroline's car was already there, parked in her usual place just as he had always remembered it. And of course, the daffodils, shyly bringing a dash of colour to the pretty garden. He hadn't wanted to arrive home burdened with sombre reminders of the hospital which might dampen the high spirits of the children. Fortunately he didn't need the ventilator but was given suction at various intervals because he lacked the strength needed to cough up phlegm. He knew from Caroline that they were in a state of excitement and anxiously prayed that he wouldn't disappoint them. More than even his first trip outside, this outing was the most terrifying of them all. Over the months, home had come to symbolise an entirely different way of life, in which he no longer belonged and with which he still lacked the courage and strength to deal. Indeed, Roy felt that this home visit had come too soon; he wasn't ready . . . and secretly feared that he might never be.

It was late March and cold. As he was helped out of the ambulance, he already yearned for the warmth and security of the ward, the peace and quiet that he knew he would never have at home, the comfort of the daily, monotonous routine. Treacherous thoughts! He tried to banish them from his mind and walked as cheerfully as he could through the hall door.

'Welcome Home Daddy.' The banner was the first thing he noticed and he felt immediately glad to return to the people he loved most. They were all there, standing taut with excitement – Alex, Rachel, Naomi – their joyful expressions tinged with a trace of anxiety. As he hobbled in on his two sticks, he stubbed his toe on the carpet, having grown used to the polished lino floor of the hospital, and fell over.

Unable to break his fall, Roy let out a cry of pain as he fell on his thumb. The grand entrance deteriorated into a ignominious scramble on the floor as everyone rushed to his assistance.

The whole day felt spoilt for Roy and his earlier intentions were forgotten. He should never have come. It was too soon.

Tensely entering the lounge, he nursed his injured thumb, filled with dread that he had broken it. The thought of painful X-rays and medical tests that would inevitably be given when he returned to the National made it hard for him to enjoy the sensation of being home. There was one moment when he was able to rise above his pain as he sat down in his armchair. There was a brief silence as if he was trying on a suit which did not yet fit. Alterations were needed until at last eyes closed and at peace, Roy lent back and savoured the sensation, while the children gazed at him with bated breath at last able to really welcome their father home for the first time.

Then the spell was broken and Roy's attention shifted back to his thumb, which he kept on examining surreptitiously. Guiltily, he stopped only when he noticed Caroline watching him, a worried frown on her face. Later to his relief, it turned out to be bruised rather than broken, but it throbbed for the whole day, relentlessly and without a pause.

Caroline had cooked a wonderful lunch – roast chicken, roast potatoes and vegetables, his favourite – but Roy looked aghast as she piled the food on his plate.

Has she forgotten that I can only eat small portions?

When he looked around everyone else was tucking into far larger quantities with obvious relish, once more he felt like an alien, a foreigner who didn't seem to fit in. He couldn't taste or enjoy any of it, and his resentment grew amidst the merrymaking. Once again, he longed for the quiet of the hospital where he really belonged.

The nurse was obviously having a great time and joined in with all of the fun but Roy grew more and more withdrawn. Although loud and boisterous, the children sensed his unease and seemed disappointed, expecting more from him than he was able to give.

Shortly after lunch Roy started to agitate to go back. They tried to persuade him to stay longer but he wouldn't and much to the relief of all he set off back to the hospital mid-afternoon. Glad to be on his way, he felt depressed and unsettled, knowing that the day had been a let-down for them all.

I'm unable to move, helpless, grumpy and certainly in no way the father or husband they remember, he reflected uneasily. *Getting back to normal is going to be more difficult than even I suspected.*

Caroline was having identical thoughts on the way back in her car. She had briefly congratulated the children for helping to make it a wonderful day but she knew that her words sounded hollow. When Roy first walked in the door, Alex had almost jumped with relief, sensing that he could discard some of his responsibility and revert to being a child again. Somewhere between that entrance and Roy's fall, he had resumed his burden picking it up again as they picked Roy off the floor. This was not the father he remembered. What had happened to him?

Chapter Nine

THE NATIONAL HOSPITAL FOR NERVOUS DISEASES REHABILITATION CENTRE

THEY ALL had to adjust their behaviour significantly and treat Roy with kid gloves. In many ways, it wasn't only the children who had set their expectations too high and Caroline reflected that it was a lesson they would all have to learn over the following months. While Roy was undoubtedly on the road to recovery, it wasn't going to happen overnight and he was only gradually able to ease his way back into the mainstream of life. Indeed, they would never be able to turn back the clock. None of them would be the same people as they were before Roy's illness and they would have to accept the negative changes along with the positive.

The transition from Intensive Care to the outside world would have to be done step by step. Initially they did think of transferring Roy for a week to the private ward in the National, but on examination it was decided to leave Roy in the Harris Unit (Intensive Care) and make him less dependent on help, ie, not helping him with dressing or eating. That done he would be ready for the next step which was a transfer to the Rehabilitation Centre at East Finchley.

East Finchley! Caroline broke the news to Roy in the same tone of voice as if he had won the national lottery.

Roy looked at his wife, all her hidden misgivings openly etched on his face. Moves, or indeed changes of any sort, were never good news, let alone marvellous.

'That means the doctors really feel that you're getting better,' she continued, her voice spoken in a more subdued tone as she realised that her plan was not going to work.

'Before you know it, you'll be able to come home,' she finished bravely, wondering if he would view that as good news or not.

Since that visit home, neither of them had suggested another one and Caroline knew that he dreaded leaving the hospital, even for a walk outside. In some ways, the illness had rendered him more than just physically vulnerable and the hospital had now become his home, his sanctity which enveloped him in its safe refuge against the uncertainties of outside life. Recognising this, the doctors decided that it was time for Roy to move on, even though he was physically still very weak.

'There's nothing further we can do medically,' Dr Wiles told them both when he came on his ward round.

'The longer people stay in hospital, the more frightened they feel about moving and believe that they will never cope on their own. Of course, we'll still keep a close eye on his progress but he would benefit far more from being in the Rehabilitation Centre at East Finchley.'

Roy made all the usual objections, stalling for time for as long as he could. However, even he recognised that he would postpone but not put off the evil day and gradually resigned himself to the transfer. On 17 March, a nurse from the Rehabilitation Centre came to Intensive Care to collect him.

'Sure, it's a grand day to be leaving,' one of the Irish nurses told him cheerfully. 'It is St Patrick's Day after all, and you never know what you might see in the way of celebrations on the journey over.'

Roy privately had little interest in St Patrick or anyone else at that moment, but he appreciated her optimism and cheerful humour. How on earth was he going to manage without the medical staff at Queen Square, supporting through all his hopelessness and despair, encouraging him to keep on trying when he frequently wanted to give up the struggle.

Caroline had taken home most of his belongings so he only had an overnight bag to take with him. She took his silver tubes and some medication. The area around his bed looked sadly deserted, much as a house for sale quickly acquires that neglected look within days of its owners moving out. The previous evening they had given the medical staff a magnum of Champagne to thank them and to 'celebrate' his departure. Apart from Roy everyone was delighted that he was well enough to leave.

'Of course we'll miss you,' the sister told him, seeing that he was not in a frame of mind to celebrate, 'but seriously Roy, you'll soon look back on this time in your life and wonder why you felt so nervous at the prospect of leaving.'

Once again, he was transported in an ambulance and had to wait for about half an hour before setting off. Needless to say, the wait merely served to increase his feelings of apprehension, and instinct told him that his new home was not going to be as comfortable or supportive as Queen Square; he could expect little of the personal attention which he had become used to with the very experienced staff in Intensive Care. Roy had been told how wonderful the centre was but was warned that he would have to do much more physical exercise than previously and was extremely nervous as to how he would cope. Standing up and sitting down took a major effort in themselves and just walking a few yards was exhausting. How would he cope with any extra activity?

In spite of all his misgivings, part of him was feeling excited. At last he was leaving hospital and taking a significant step towards leading a normal life again. He had been cut off from London for seven months and now, as the ambulance finally started up, he was able to see everything again. They passed the familiar sights in Russell Square, Euston Road, where they stopped to collect some more patients and on to Swiss Cottage, Fitzjohns Avenue, Whitestone Pond . . . Roy almost called out the names of the streets in sheer delight, joy at seeing the city again temporarily over-riding his fears. He hadn't realised how much he missed the bustle and teeming crowds and for the first time experienced a longing to rejoin life again.

They arrived at the centre at lunchtime but his euphoria in the ambulance evaporated as quickly as it had arisen. Wheeled into the dining room full of unfamiliar faces, Roy's heart sank. He was going to have to start all over again making new relationships, an effort that called on limited resources already fully engaged in the struggle of building up his own strength and body functions. The other patients introduced themselves to Roy and tried to make him feel at home, but he froze inside, longing to escape. From the quiet warmth of the Intensive Care unit, the centre appeared impersonal, noisy and bordering on the chaotic with streams of people and general noise. At last, Roy felt an intense urge to go home and vowed that he would work extra hard so as to be able to leave the centre as early as possible.

It was certainly a rude awakening into life. The high Victorian ceilings of the Rehabilitation Centre and its dimly lit, poorly decorated and cold rooms were such a contrast to the bright modern atmosphere of Queen Square. To his horror, he had to share a bedroom with five others, a gloomy draughty room that radiated little in the way of welcoming warmth. Roy hid behind a book and spoke little, conscious of appearing rude but unused to being with so many people after the relative isolation of the previous months. He still found social intercourse difficult, particularly amongst such a diverse group where patients came from all walks of life.

While the staff tried to involve him as much as possible, they recognised that he would need a period of adjustment and didn't push him too hard for the first few days until he began to relax. The nurses were kind but unwilling to mother him along and he was expected to make more of an effort to help himself. One of them gave him a brief tour that first afternoon, ending up in the lounge area where there was a television. Unlike at Queen Square, smoking was permitted which affected Roy's breathing. Once his guide had returned to her duties, Roy fled. He couldn't breathe properly, disliked the programme on television and, not wishing to air his grievance on the first day, sought refuge in a second, much smaller lounge. Finding a seat by the window, he settled down to read his book, preferring by far his own company. It was here that Caroline found him when she arrived later that afternoon. Like Roy she was shocked by the old, shabby and cold building and was determined that he should come home as quickly as he could. To her surprise, Roy showed the first sign of wanting to return home as well, and was full of resolution to work hard at the physiotherapy.

Maybe Dr Wiles was right, Caroline mused to herself as she carried in some of Roy's belongings. Being in the centre will give him the push he needs to get out of here. He'd never have wanted to go home if he hadn't come here in the first place.

'I've brought you some supper,' she told him, glad of something to talk about other than his new rather grim surroundings. 'I'll find out about kitchen facilities tomorrow but the soup in the thermos is hot.'

Caroline and Roy had also both decided that she would spend less time with him and more with the children, especially Naomi. With intensive occupational and physiotherapy, his days were much fuller so that he was less reliant on her for company. However, she still came in to bring him lunch and again during the evening staying until he went to bed. She felt that he would get more nutritious meals if she made them at home, and the liquidised soups were more suitable, given his limited capacity to eat solid food. Caroline suctioned him prior to leaving at night and made him comfortable, taking the place of the nurse with amazing competence, and compensating for the lack of individual nursing care that he no longer had. The evenings were long and lonely and he was grateful to have Caroline by his side, although he suspected that she was bored stiff during those long hours.

She's never complained once, he reflected, feeling a twinge of guilt for the first time. *To think of the hours that she's sat by my bed while I slept! Would I have supported her with the same selflessness had our positions been reversed?*

It was a question that none of them could answer. Had he been asked a year ago, if he would survive eight months in hospital, completely paralysed, he might well have answered no. When the worst imaginable situation arose, you somehow just knuckled down and coped with it, stepping into a different consciousness and mode of functioning. Now, as the illness was really beginning to retreat, they both felt even more overwhelmed than they had during the more critical stages. Whatever stress–coping resources they had summoned to assist in the beginning seemed to have finally run dry, and the body was demanding the rest that it undoubtedly needed after such a traumatic period.

Roy soon established a sort of routine at East Finchley. The staff actually made a point of ensuring that his days were completely predictable but refused to allow him to get too comfortable and complacent.

'He needs to be ready to deal with the outside world,' the physio explained to Caroline. 'Although his existence here is quite predictable, once he goes into the outside world he'll have to be more flexible, he's certainly learned in the past few months how unpredictable life can be.'

It was hard work but they did allow him certain safety nets. After Caroline left in the evening, he was given a bell to use in case of an emergency. He would ring about twice in the night to be turned – just having it there was a tremendous reassurance. At seven o'clock they were all woken with a cup of tea and medications. To his pride and pleasure, there was no medication for him.

Now there's progress for you, he thought happily, as he watched his fellow patients swallow endless small capsules.

Caroline was equally pleased, neither of them having ever been particularly 'pill-minded' and relieved that he didn't have to take such strong medication indefinitely.

Breakfast was at eight-thirty, by which time they were expected to be ready and dressed. Roy needed every minute to accomplish this one task, and he was often late as it was. Trying to wash and shave, brush his teeth and dress, small routine activities that he had previously done without thinking, had become momentous chores, and left him so exhausted that he often felt like going back to bed again when he had finished. Remembering his resolution to get home as quickly as possible, he summoned all his resources to get to the dining room, where he would collapse gratefully in weary silence. Marmalade, cereals, stewed fruit, toast – he still couldn't taste the food properly but was gratified to notice that at least he could recognise the difference between marmalade and jam again. Things were definitely improving.

After breakfast, he had an hour of physiotherapy where he had to do exercise after exercise to build up his muscular strength. Press-ups, standing up from a sitting position, lifting weights, moving the hips from side to side, sitting and balancing on a large plastic ball, strengthening the legs . . . whenever he felt like giving up he remembered his matchstick thighs and carried on with renewed determination.

Then morning tea which was spent watching television. At first, Roy had been amazed at this steady trail of people who drifted towards the lounge at eleven, as if drawn towards some strange magnetic force which they were unable to resist. Then he found himself following suit.

'You're really becoming institutionalised,' Caroline laughed when he told her about this one evening. 'I can just picture it, glued to the television, whatever happens to flash across the screen, cigarette in one hand, coffee in the other . . .'

Roy laughed, comfortably in the knowledge that he wouldn't be there long enough to fit into her vividly painted little vignette. Had she realised the mindlessness of most of the programmes they watched without discrimination, she would have been reinforced in her opinion. None the less, Roy quickly discovered the value behind such a pattern, which he tried to explain in defence of his fellow patients.

'We have little to say to each other,' he remarked. 'When you've been here for weeks on end, you don't have much to talk about other than your illness, and that can either be too painful and personal, or such common knowledge as to be incredibly tedious. The television is a nice, socially acceptable way of being with people without any obligation to talk.'

'Surely you could talk about lots of things,' she argued, 'like your outside lives, business, politics . . .?'

'Oh yes, and some of them do, especially the ones who are better and are about to leave. Occasionally, the conversation can be really stimulating and we'll all join in, but for the most part, we're so exhausted after a morning of physiotherapy that it's too much of an effort to concentrate, and television is such an easy substitute. It's just the sort of passive stimulation I need after doing twenty press-ups.'

Caroline nodded, understanding what he was saying and able to relate it to herself. How many evenings had she longed to go home and vegetate in front of some film on television. By the time she had spent time with the children, made out her daily lists, caught up with telephone calls and tackled countless other niggling tasks, she was usually too tired to even do that and opted for her bed instead. Many of the patients were recovering from strokes, tumours, or in for respite care and suffering from multiple sclerosis and other serious illnesses and it was often the case that they were so tied up with their own pain and problems that there was no incentive to communicate. They just wanted to be left alone to nurse their wounds, both literally and metaphorically, and any fears Roy might have had with regard to his privacy being invaded were soon dispelled.

Occasionally, Roy would strike up a conversation with one or two of his neighbours. It usually sobered him considerably, as he realised how fortunate he was.

At least I can expect a full recovery, he thought with increasing confidence.

With each day, his strength was growing and his body functions returning one by one. In contrast many of the other patients were facing a lifetime of disability, interspersed with recurrent episodes of their illness. Some of them seemed to be so courageous and cheerful that he felt ashamed of his own despair and misery.

Lunch was served at twelve-thirty, and Roy would enjoy homemade soup, brought in by Caroline while the other patients ate the somewhat unappetising food from the canteen. Even more enjoyable was to have her there for the hour, and he felt renewed and refreshed by the time she left to return home. After lunch was occupational therapy, where he was encouraged to play chess on a board pinned on to the wall. This ingenious device forced him to stretch his arms and fingers in order to move the pieces, a way of strengthening his muscles which was much more enjoyable and gentle than lifting weights. If the weather permitted they would do light gardening, digging up the vegetable patch and planting flowers and vegetables. Spring had truly arrived and the mild breeze warmed up his body, feeling considerably bruised after the severe battering of the winter months in hospital. He tired easily and would periodically lean on his spade, turn his face up towards the sun and drink in its gentle warmth and feeling a sense of well-being for the first time since his holiday.

On less clement days, they did arts and crafts. Roy made a footstool and carried on with more printing, the object being to strengthen his hands and arms in particular. Then another session of physiotherapy where he repeated his exercises of the morning. By the end of the afternoon, Roy felt as if he had done a hard day's work and staggered into the lounge with his book.

Indeed, Roy tempered his earlier opinion of East Finchley, as he became used to the centre. While it wasn't especially comfortable or attractive, it had a definite pragmatic attraction and an air of getting down to business. He valued the efficient and encouraging manner of the staff and worked hard, determined to be able to attend as an outpatient at the soonest possible date.

At last the time had come when Roy could sleep his first night at home. It was a tense time but Queen Square kindly sent Rachel, the nursing sister, to spend the first night at home with them in order to see whether Caroline and Roy could cope on their own. He still needed suction occasionally and to be turned two or three times during the night.

That first night, they whispered together, determined to manage on their own without calling the nurse. Both of them desperately wanted to prove that it was viable, that Roy would be able to return home and really start getting back to normal. At first Roy lay quietly, not wanting to disturb Caroline and yet knowing that it was time to be turned. He moved his legs restlessly and she was immediately awake and beside the bed.

'Is it time yet?' she whispered, while he nodded unable to speak because of the silver tube inserted in his trachea to facilitate breathing.

Expertly, having been taught by the nurses, Caroline turned him gently over. Once he was comfortable, she returned to her bed, exhausted but excited, pleased to have him home at last. Shortly after managing to fall asleep she was awoken again, this time to suction him as he was having difficulty breathing. Then up an hour and a half later to turn him again . . . it was a long night and the next morning she appeared at breakfast with dark shadows under her eyes.

'You didn't call me,' the nurse accused her, having slept through the entire night.

'We didn't need to,' Caroline replied calmly, a smile on her face. 'We managed it on our own and there was no problem.'

'Hmm . . .' Rachel said dubiously, looking at Caroline's pale and drawn face. 'I don't doubt your ability to cope with Roy; it's how you'll manage after weeks of no sleep.'

'Oh, I'll be fine,' Caroline said hastily.

Rachel made no comment, but as she was leaving sat down to speak to both of them.

'I think Roy is ready to come home and I'll recommend it to the hospital and East Finchley. However, I do think that you should consider getting in a night nurse, even if only to turn Roy. Without your sleep, you won't be much use to anyone, Caroline.'

Both of them hesitated, reluctant to have a stranger in their home any more, even if only for the night. However, that evening they discussed it in more depth and eventually agreed. Given the go-ahead, Roy moved home after Easter and they got in a night nurse for the next two months.

'It's such a waste of time,' Roy grumbled. 'She just sits there for most of the night, getting up to turn me twice. She must be so bored.'

'It's what she's paid to do,' Caroline observed firmly. 'I've noticed that she comes armed with books, knitting and other means to keep her awake.'

Having agreed, and unable to come up with any better suggestions, Roy dropped the subject, secretly finding it a relief to have an expert at hand all night. With the silver tube inserted in his trachea during the night, Roy was unable to speak but attracted her attention by banging on the bed. Caroline had moved into Rachel's room so that she could have undisturbed sleep. The first few nights passed smoothly enough but this was rudely interrupted towards the end of that week.

It was just after Passover and Caroline had packed a kitchen cupboard too full with the special crockery and cutlery taken out for the festival. As they all lay asleep upstairs, and the night nurse sat engrossed in her book, there was an almighty crash from downstairs. Quaking with fear, her head filled with visions of unwelcome intruders, the nurse forced herself to go downstairs. To her absolute amazement, no one else had heard the noise. She timidly opened the kitchen door, not knowing what to expect and to her utter relief she found the remains of a huge blue and white dish smashed into tiny pieces on the floor. She swiftly found the brush and pan and swept up the remains of what must have at one time been a rather lovely piece of china. Fortunately the remaining two months passed without mishap and the night nurse left in June. Since Roy's return home, the au pair had also left, much to Caroline's relief. The family were alone at last.

It was during these two months that Roy felt a tremendous urge to go to synagogue. It was on the Festival of Shavout (the Giving of the Law) that he dressed himself in a suit, unable to put on a tie due to the silver tube still being in place, he tied a smart cravat round his neck – he still needed a walking stick to steady himself. Rabbi Levy was pleased to welcome the complete family back to the very caring community that had supported them so steadfastly during their time of darkness. It is the custom for members of the family to stand up when a father or grandfather is called up to the Tebah to read from the Torah. On this occasion, word had circulated that Roy was going to attend for the first time since his illness. The synagogue was packed, the warmth of welcome could be felt instantly and when Roy was 'called up' to the Tebah, the whole community rose in unison. Tears of gratitude, relief and thanks to God for his safe return were rolling down Caroline's cheeks. Her cousin, Susan put her arm around her to comfort her.

One didn't need to say anything now, as, in the past, actions spoke louder than words.

The children had greeted Roy's return with ambivalence. Although excited to have their father back, there was nevertheless a slight reservation in them all. Home in body, he was so concerned with his own well-being that he had little time or patience for his family and was difficult to live with. There were endless complaints first thing in the morning as he struggled to get dressed and demanded assistance to be lifted in and out of the bath; constant small errands and demands; Roy would shout at them one minute and then ask them to help him on some personal task the next, as if nothing had happened. Always volatile, he had become explosive and permanently on edge. As a result, the children crept resentfully around the house, not daring to challenge him in any way.

Caroline's patience ran thin until she finally snapped. It was one thing to be patient while visiting a person in hospital but far more difficult when he was home under your feet all day.

'That's it,' she shouted one day, as Roy demanded that she help him to do up his shoelace right away, even though she was in the middle of cooking lunch.

He would never countenance any delay in his orders and she suddenly became furious.

'I am *not* your servant, here to do your bidding if and when you like. Nor, I might add are the children. It's about time you stopped depending on others and got on with it yourself.'

Expecting a violent display of temper, she was surprised to notice that Roy had grown quiet, and hoped that she hadn't gone too far. He seemed to take it to heart and, when she dropped him at East Finchley, was quite subdued. The words had some effect and she noticed a definite effort on his behalf not to snap at her although he was less restrained with the children. It was as if the months of enforced silence had built up inside him and he was venting all of his pent-up irritations, frustration all at once. Alex grew tense and angry, Naomi tearful and Rachel stubborn and bellicose. Uncertain what to do, Caroline rang Eric for advice, knowing that Roy's partner was someone she could confide in without feeling that she was betraying her husband to an outsider.

Chapter Ten

THOUGHTS OF RETURNING TO WORK

'HE NEEDS to get back to work,' Eric counselled her.

'Work? He can hardly walk or talk. I suspect that work is still a long way off. Besides, he's stopped agitating about the office and doesn't seem in too much of a hurry to go back.'

'Exactly,' Eric exclaimed. 'I bet he's feeling really disorientated and at a loose end. Having been very much in control, not only here in the office, but also at home, he has been whipped out of life for eight months, and now has somehow to fit back into his old role. He can't, not only because he has changed but so have you. The sooner he builds up his self-confidence and becomes actively involved in something completely, apart from hospitals and botulism, the better.'

Eric agreed to come around with the latest copy of the *Estates Gazette* which Roy was still reading and to invite him to come in to the office one afternoon. Knowing how much Roy hated to have things sprung upon him unexpectantly, Caroline paved the way the night before.

'Eric wants you to go into the office for an afternoon, just to say hello and look around,' she said casually. 'Why not go this Friday afternoon, you're at home anyway and I could go in with you?'

'No, not Friday,' he insisted. 'I'm usually far too tired.'

'What about Wednesday then?'

'No, I . . .' Roy stuttered, racking his brains for an excuse. She waited patiently, knowing that he was putting off the day.

'I don't want them seeing me like this,' he said firmly and no amount of persuasion would make him change his mind, even when Eric tried the following day.

However, the seed had been planted and that in itself was enough for the present. Roy still seemed uninterested in the practicalities of everyday life, leaving Caroline to manage the accounts and business side of the household, a role he had previously always filled with an almost arrogant exclusiveness. Since his illness, Caroline's confidence had increased tenfold. She had spoken as an equal to those doctors and had survived months of running a home, family and nursing Roy. That he let her continue seemed to be almost natural and she found herself enjoying the new challenges that it gave her. She was becoming increasingly aware that Roy also needed to have a goal and a sense of purpose and refused to allow him to complacently rely on her. Nor would she let the children constantly do small things for him; although they all desperately wanted to make life easier and more comfortable for him; they forced themselves to stand back and be hard. Roy's homecoming was not as comfortable as he had imagined it might be.

'You just have to get out and speak,' she said brusquely when Roy complained that he was too self-conscious to talk in front of strangers. 'It's only with practice that your voice will return to normal and you'll regain full mobility of the facial muscles.'

'It's the old perfectionist in you,' Caroline smiled having just appeared with his lunch. 'It's hard to be content with second best but it looks like you have no choice for the moment.'

Roy scowled, knowing that what Caroline said was relevant, not only for speech. Since his illness, he had been forced to compromise, to ease off on the drive towards perfection not only for himself, but also for others. That tolerance and clemency, usually a sign of the mellowing with age, had been forced on him prematurely and he struggled to make them his own. Unwillingly at first to accept his limitations, Roy was slowly realising that it was the only way he would ever really recover.

I've got to be gentle not only with others, but myself, he thought slowly, this kind of thinking totally alien to his hard masculinity.

Indeed, once he became conscious of the subtle shift, Roy even began to enjoy it. He liked sharing equal responsibility with Caroline, appreciating her opinion in areas where it previously would neither have been sought, offered, nor accepted. He enjoyed releasing his iron control in the office, and reawakened the elaborate plans for his new position if and when he returned to work. He began to notice and appreciate things he'd never had time to observe before . . . like the trees in the garden, the dawn chorus of the birds with the coming spring, the complete works of Shakespeare on the bookcase in the lounge, there for display but never read from start to finish until now. Everything was seen with fresh eyes, new feeling, discerning thought. His close dalliance with death gave everything a more vivid splendour, just as love for a person or thing can increase dramatically the moment you are about to lose them. He lived fully in the present, relishing every moment when he was without pain, when the sun shone, when he accomplished yet another difficult task. Small, insignificant tasks now yielded as much pleasure as those of more import, as he fully understood how transient and temporary life could be.

Exasperated, critical and at times hard on him, Caroline nonetheless supported Roy every step of the way. They were closer now than ever before and as he began to regain his confidence and his ability to survive independently of medical or human props, they became a real partnership, able to give more to each other than before the illness. It was a strange interlude in their lives, painful and exhausting for both Roy and the whole family, but also incredibly rich and rewarding.

'So when are you going to come in and see us?' Eric persisted, asking the same question of Roy every visit.

'Soon, soon,' Roy replied vaguely, a hint of panic flickering across his eyes as he turned away from his partner's scrutinising gaze.

'The sooner you meet everyone again, the easier it will be, you know Roy,' Eric said, determined not to be fobbed off. 'If you really mean to start back again in September, you're going to have to take the plunge to visit soon.'

'Yes,' Roy agreed noncommittally.

'And I've discussed some of your ideas about moving more into public relations and everyone seems to be really enthusiastic about it,' he continued. 'It's just what we need at the moment as we've got to keep building up new business. It's not as if this property boom is going to continue indefinitely and we need to be firmly established when it crashes.'

'I don't know,' Roy remarked, a shade of bitterness in his voice. 'You've coped rather well so far.'

That the office had managed all too well without him was largely due to the property boom which had hit England just as Roy fell ill and was playing havoc with prices and rents. His initial fears that the business would fold up had been replaced by equally real feelings of inadequacy, of not being needed at all.

Eric burst out laughing, realising immediately what was wrong.

'Oh come on, Roy,' he smiled, 'you'd never have forgiven us if we'd let the business fold up while you were in hospital. It doesn't mean that we don't need you and while we've been ticking over very nicely during the past year, we desperately need your experience in the agency department if we're to hold our own against all the competition.'

Relieved that he could return in a new capacity, rather than trying to slot back into an old role, Roy had set the first week in September as his date, hoping to start back at first part-time and gradually increasing the hours. It was sufficiently far away not to cause him too much anxiety yet, while part of him was actually looking forward to the office again, the year out having refreshed him and allowed him to develop a new perspective. None the less, he knew that he still needed a few more months over the summer in which to build up his strength, both physically and mentally.

They both did. Caroline, as much as Roy, desperately needed a holiday and they chose a week in June, just the two of them, to visit Warminster. It was an important week, for it marked the cutting of the last of the ties with the hospital. Dr Wiles had been reluctant to close up the tracheostomy site in case of complications and he needed to open it again. Now, before going on holiday, it was essential to close it up and hope that once the tube was taken out the wound would heal and knit properly.

Unfortunately, the site had been open for such a long time that the edges of the skin had sealed themselves and did not knit together as expected. But, with time, the area did finally heal and Roy's voice returned to a reasonably normal tone as there was no longer any escape of air when he spoke. This took place only days before their planned trip in the country but made all the difference to their holiday.

The summer so far had been particularly bad but Roy and Caroline were fortunately lucky. The weather was lovely and they were able to get out for walks in the fresh air. Roy also used the opportunity to start driving again, first in the driveway of the hotel they were staying in and later on along the winding country lanes.

'Not on the motorway, mind you,' he insisted, lacking the confidence to handle the car at speed.

However, he surprised himself at how quickly it all came back, and before he realised what was happening, he was on the motorway. As he turned the car expertly outside their house at the end of the journey home, he turned proudly to Caroline, expecting some sort of congratulations.

'Right, that's it,' she said, a twinkle in her eyes, but her expression othewise dead-pan. 'I'm not driving you to East Finchley any more.'

Roy looked at her aghast, his old fear of the new raising itself immediately. But he soon regained his confidence completely and enjoyed the independence. His progress with physiotherapy was such that by the end of June he was advised to join a local gym outside the NHS where he could tone-up the muscles throughout the body by weightlifting, rather than spending the time in physiotherapy. These weights were considerably heavier than the ones in the physiotherapy department and Roy sensed ruefully that the hard work had only just begun. He persisted at it, attending the gym for an hour three days a week and returned to the centre at the end of July for a check-up. So impressed was the physiotherapist at his progress that she suggested he sign off for any further treatment from Queen Square and she would make a report to Dr Wiles ready for his next visit in September.

Life was returning to normality with almost frightening speed. For the first time since his illness, Caroline and Roy started to go out socially, although neither of them could cope with late nights and made a point of coming home early. Not that they went out that often, for Roy was still self-conscious of his wasted body and emaciation, despite assurance from the others that he looked fine.

The office started to send Roy paperwork, as much to get him used to the idea of returning to work as to build up his concentration. He was grateful for the exercise, noticing that he tired easily as much mentally as physically.

At times it all became too much for him and he would explode, shouting at the children for making too much noise, or would fall into a deep depression.

'It's so unfair,' he would complain bitterly to his family. 'I've lost a year of my life and I'm still not able to walk properly or to concentrate on something as simple as a crossword. I'll never be the same again. I still look like a physical wreck.'

They would then reassure him, repeating the same words of comfort that it was taking time but that he would soon be fine.

'Look how far you've come since Easter,' Caroline pointed out. 'You're getting better so quickly now compared to the snail-like progress you were making before.'

He had heard it all before but nonetheless found her words soothing and took heart from them. The children found it more difficult, unable to understand or to handle his sudden fits of anger and temper. Previously, Roy had always helped them with their homework, spending hours sitting with them for encouragement. While he did shout and overpower them at times, they enjoyed his interest and were happy when the time given had been fruitful. Now, he was unable to concentrate or offer much of himself to them and they found it confusing and upsetting. Many of their interchanges had become negative, the shouting and anger without any of the positive aspects of the creative Roy.

September was looming frighteningly near, bringing with it the discipline of getting up early, of travelling to the office, of exhausting paperwork. None of it held much appeal to Roy at the moment. Would he be able to re-establish a niche for himself, a niche so adequately filled by his colleagues in his absence? He would have to get used to new staff and changes, to fit in with new ways that had been established. Refusing Caroline's suggestion to seek help from a psychiatrist, the subject was closed once more and Roy battled away with his physical problems. Unlike Caroline, he didn't want to think about any psychological difficulties and focused instead on the ever-immediate present and his practical difficulties.

Chapter Eleven

SUMMER HOLIDAYS

TOWARDS THE end of July, there were real changes, noticed and appreciated even by Roy who was his own worst critic. For the first time, he could bathe without assistance, walk for up to half an hour at a time and swim, although he still found that activity painful. It was somewhat tentatively that Caroline finally plucked up the courage to raise the question of their annual holiday.

'Holiday.'

'I know you might not feel much in the mood for going away, but it's important to the children and it might do you good as well,' she explained.

Privately, she hoped that the holiday might help to heal the breach that was growing up between Roy and the children. He had missed out on a whole year of their lives, during which time they had grown up and matured, already older in their years as a result of the strain of the last year. Roy and Alex were constantly clashing, as his father refused to recognise that he was growing up, no longer the little boy of the previous year. Rachel and Roy also often came to loggerheads, as he directed a fair share of his anger and frustration at her, while at the same time demanding her time and help in getting dressed and generally looking after him. Only Naomi emerged relatively unscathed, escaping the great periods of wrath.

'Aren't you lucky to be deaf,' Rachel grumbled at her little sister after being yelled at by her father for getting yet again another bad report. 'At least you don't have to listen to him.'

It wasn't strictly true, for despite her deafness, she somehow managed to hear Roy's outbursts. They all did, and the household was shaken and subdued for several hours after he had lost his temper. Caroline prayed that it was temporary, aware that the school-work of the children would undoubtedly suffer as a result, not to mention the general strain under which they were living.

She had come up with the idea of a holiday as one way of bringing about a reconciliation and wasn't to be disappointed. Roy agreed, somewhat reluctantly at first, and they booked their usual three weeks in August. They decided not to venture abroad with aeroplanes and the hazard of in-flight meals, but to stay closer to home and chose Torquay in Cornwall, which had a warm climate, picturesque walks and beautiful scenery. Before they left, Roy did go into the office to see his colleagues and whilst he was there received a surprised phone call from a client . . .

'Is that you, Roy?' he exclaimed. 'I thought you were dead . . .'

He was very much alive and, as they packed for the holiday, Caroline noticed some of his old humour reasserting itself.

'And . . . we're taking a packed lunch for the journey this time,' he grumbled, a smile on his face.

She let out a sigh; it felt like she had been holding her breath for the past week. Suddenly she knew that it was going to be all right. Already the seeds of a new relationship between Roy and the children was developing as all three of them helped Roy to pack for the first time, crushing his shirts as they squeezed them into the suitcase, destroying the usual order of his wardrobe. To her amaze-ment Roy sat by with an amused expression on his face.

She hadn't been wrong and the holiday was a great success. They managed to do things as a family again and, although Roy tired easily, he seemed to enjoy himself as much as the children. All Caroline wanted was to bask in the sunshine and rest her aching body, and they all returned refreshed and ready to tackle life again. They arrived home as usual on the August Bank Holiday weekend, giving Roy that Monday to prepare himself for the office. September was already on top of them and there was a sense of excitement at the prospect of new classes in school, new timetables, new begin-nings. On 30th Tuesday August 1988, exactly one year late, Roy put on his suit and went to work.

EPILOGUE

THE PANIC is over. We are now two sets of GCSEs, two sets of A
Levels, one house move and one legal case later. Is anything remotely
comparable to the terrible experience that we all suffered? I have
to say all because although Roy was the patient and the one who
suffered so terribly, physically, mentally and emotionally, we, his
family, who were part of his support system, also suffered.

In the early days of Roy's illness, in fact, the day after his diagnosis,
the public health laboratory in Colindale immediately sent a doctor
to inspect the airline we were travelling on and the supplier of the
contaminated food. They very swiftly organised for the withdrawal
from all airlines of trays of 'food' from this particular caterer. These
were all examined and an extremely high percentage of them were
found to be contaminated by bacteria. None of them, it may be
added, contained the botulinum toxin but it was fairly conclusive
that the toxin did emanate from the food. The main questions were
– was the toxin in the food before it was packed or did it enter
during the production or canning process (the meal in question was
contained in an aluminium receptacle similar to a can of sardines
and opened in a similar fashion)? Was the botulism the fault of the
cabin crew who might not have heated the food to the appropriate
temperature?

It became fairly evident after Colindale had tested all the remaining packs of food that the fault did lay at the door of the caterer.
They were based in Switzerland. However, in an international incident like this which had very quickly become interesting and international news, the caterers were visited by the health authorities,

found to have a fault in their canning process and very shortly afterwards were forced to close down.

We were advised to sue. After all here was Roy lying paralysed in a hospital bed unable to do anything for himself. Someone would pay for what was quite obviously a very serious mistake. Who does one sue? Is it the airline company, who had incidentally kept an extremely low profile during the whole period of Roy's illness (I would imagine lest they should make themselves look like the guilty party) or should we sue the caterer, who was based in Switzerland?

In the early months I was very reluctant to do anything, but we did have a number of legal friends who were able to give us the benefit of their experience. A letter was written to the airline, who very quickly denied liability. Letters went backwards and forth for a number of weeks with very little joy. One of our friends suggested that I should consult a particular firm of solicitors in Lincoln's Inn who specialised in airline cases. I duly made an appointment, had a very interesting and what I thought productive discussion. Yes, they were very interested to take on the case. In their opinion we had great justification and felt it was one which they could win for us. That same evening I received a telephone call from one of the partners to say that on further reflection they were unable to take on the case, as their firm had previously signed an agreement with this major airline to the effect that they would never act against them.

Roy, at that time, still lying prostrate was adamant that we should use his old school friend Alan who was a solicitor, not specialising in negligence cases which this quite obviously was, but having a small practice in South London. In his experience, he felt, if one goes to these large firms of solicitors you start with the partner who then in turn passes your case to someone else and you lose the personal contact. In Alan's case he was a 'one man band'. Not only that but if anyone was going to 'fight' for Roy it would be Alan. They had known each other for 40 years. Alan it was to be.

The judgement was right. Despite our consulting a senior QC who gave us very little hope, it was Alan who found one word, an entré whereby the airline company did assume responsibility. After all the food was served on their aircraft. The airline ticket had been bought in good faith.

The settlement was finally made out of court because Roy did not want to pursue the airline company any further. He was now back to comparative good health and he did not want to draw out this extremely long and emotionally draining legal battle. It was quite evident that if he had died I would have been a rich woman, if someone had badly slandered him he would have been a rich man. A sum was finally agreed which, once solicitor's costs were deducted, seemed quite incomparable to the amount of suffering he had been through. However, normal living was within his grasp again, life was for living, not for fighting what he felt was an unfair legal system. The decision was made. We all felt it was best to wind up this period of darkness in his life and start his second half-century in a positive fashion.

Many people have said to me, 'I don't know how you managed to keep going for so long, I couldn't have.' I have found over the years that one is amazed at the capacity of the body and mind. Physically I kept going because I felt that I could not crack. There were so many people who were dependant on me, primarily Roy whose microcosmic world consisted of his own welfare, the four walls in which he was imprisoned, the doctors, his own wretchedness but primarily the use of me as an extension of him, a mouthpiece for his feelings and anxieties. Then there was Alex who had started his first year of GCSE studies.

Fortunately, his school was based in the City of London so he was able to drop in and see Roy daily on his way home from school. He now assumed the role of 'man of the family' and naturally, being the eldest, spread a protective wing over his two younger sisters. However, it was very difficult for him emotionally. He had always been close to his father but he was now growing up without his support. In the early days he had found it very difficult to come to terms with the fact that his father was an invalid. I kept on telling him that he would recover but why was it taking so long? Could he really believe me? During the period of recovery the reality of the situation presented itself. No, Roy did not want to see his schoolwork. No, Roy did not want to know what was going on at school. No, he could not have a proper 'fight' with his sisters, lest there was too much noise. There were all these no's. What was happening? His father had left hospital and was at home with them but he was always so angry and unapproachable. He looked so weak, so vulnerable. Would he ever have his father back again as he was before. The answer is that yes he did return but two years too late.

In that time Alex was two years older, more mature, less dependant. This was a period in his life which I feel Alex learned a lot from but one in which he lost a great deal paternally.

Our eldest daughter was at the difficult age. Temperamentally she is most similar to Roy. Being a middle child the knocks come from both sides and she often voiced her protests most vehemently. If there was an argument or shouting in the family, it would most likely come from Roy and Rachel having a disagreement. We always said that they had these disagreements because they loved to spar with each other knowing exactly how far they could go. When Rachel came to visit Roy in hospital her task was to comb his wispy long hair – only Rachel could do it the way Roy liked. When Roy came home it was Rachel who he would shout at but then in the next breath ask her to help him get dressed. Rachel it was who always knew where to scratch Roy in the right place. For a long time life was very confusing for her. Life at school was not easy, life at home was so changeable. Again, those lost months at a time when fathers should be there for their daughters, time never recovered, but perhaps a time when Rachel realised how much her father needed her.

For Naomi, our younger daughter, a time to prove herself. As previously mentioned, Naomi had become deaf at the age of 19 months through meningitis. Although Naomi had been attending a school for the deaf, we had always wanted to bring her back into a mainstream hearing school. Instinctively we knew she was bright enough to cope, with the right help, and we had planned to change her school that September. We had organised for her to have support teachers sitting in the class with her for part of the time and I had intended to help her, if there were problems, when she came home from school. This was not to be. In fact, I probably felt more torn in half about Naomi than I did about anything else. We had planned over the years, this was the right age to take her out of special school if she were going to succeed. How could this happen now when I had put so much time, energy and determination into her? Apart from speaking to Naomi's teachers frequently there was very little I could do in those early months. Fortunately for us she was in a very caring school and we have a daughter who was determined to prove herself. She did manage to keep up with the schoolwork and is still in mainstream schooling. When Naomi came to visit

Roy in hospital she was our interpreter, she could lip-read when we were unable to decipher what Roy was trying to mouth. It was she who brought a cheerful smile with her every time she visited, because Naomi is lucky enough to have a brother and sister who protected her she was comparatively cushioned by Roy's illness but confused and unhappy that we were just not there.

I have always been a fairly active person but those months of looking after Roy and coping with his terrible anger and resentment took its toll. There were times, after Roy had come home that I just could not contain my anger. Why had I spent so many weeks and months looking after someone who was so ungrateful, so ungracious? Someone who found fault with every single thing I did. I didn't have a husband any more just an old man who could not be pleased, who was so sorry for himself, so unpleasant to live with and then . . . there was the old Roy, the man I married, the humour, the twinkle in his eye. We travelled backwards and forth like this for quite some time.

I started to have trouble with my teeth and gums, my digestion in my colon and then with my eyes. I remember one morning I woke up and could not open my eyes for at least five minutes. This went on for a few days and I went to see my GP. 'That sounds very strange,' he said and referred me to a neurologist. 'Come in Mrs Hayim,' he said. When I told him my complaint he asked me if I had experienced any undue stress recently! What an understatement! Of course, he had heard about Roy's illness as, it seemed, had most of the medical profession I subsequently came across. 'Mrs Hayim, just go over to the couch and take off your top clothes.' 'I've come about my eyes,' I said. 'I know that,' he said, 'but you should know that all the nervous system in the body is connected.' I most certainly did. He tested my reflexes and could find nothing wrong, but suggested that as a precaution I should have a brain scan, which I duly had. Fortunately the scan was normal. As it happened the eyes gradually improved and there was nothing wrong with them. All these problems were a direct effect of the nervous energy I had exerted, the fact that I had lived on a knife edge for so long. The body is only a machine, when you over exert it, parts of it start to give way and protest.

Is anything remotely comparable to Roy's illness? I think not. I remember one day, months into Roy's illness when Dr Wiles took me to one side. 'Mrs Hayim,' he said. 'Roy is so depressed, he doesn't respond to any of the nurses, he is not interested in anything. We can't lose him after such a long struggle. He has to snap out of his lethargy and despair otherwise he will not have the willpower to live.'

That is really what it was all about: 'THE WILL TO LIVE', the disheartening, long, slow, tedious road back to normality. The difficult part was to always appear optimistic when I knew that the obstacles that beset him were life-threatening. To sit by his bedside when I really yearned to be with the children. To always be alert when my mind and body were exhausted.

In coping with all of Roy's problems I suddenly found a new awareness in myself. Roy had always been the one who paid the bills, repaired anything that went wrong in the house, attended special meetings we had with the children's teachers, changed the light bulbs and electric plugs. Out of necessity, I could now do all these things. There was no turning back, I had grown into a much more positive, capable person, but at a price.

Having been snatched from the 'jaws of death' we have asked ourselves several questions. Why did it happen? Was it chance or was it ordained? Whatever the answer, we know that Roy had been given another chance and for this we are all immensely grateful. Mentally and physically Roy is scarred, however, life has been good to us in so many ways and it is only by positive thinking and looking around at others who are less fortunate than ourselves that we are able to say, yes, it was a very trying and difficult phase in our life, but then, we are lucky enough to have come through and now we have to get on with the rest of it.

ACKNOWLEDGEMENTS

OUR VERY grateful thanks to all the doctors, nurses, physiotherapists and occupational therapists in the Edgware General Hospital and the National Hospital for Nervous Diseases, Queen Square, London WC1 for all their support, patience and above all faith that I would live to tell the tale. My thanks to Florence, Caroline's mother, for helping with three very active children and being of tremendous moral support to Caroline. Our thanks to all our relations and numerous friends who spent hours, week after week, at my bedside trying to cheer us both through those terrible days.

On the production side, our thanks to Arlene Seaton for the hours she spent with us in the early days composing and typing out the first draft. Our thanks to Sara Hollwey for her help in re-drafting and her sensitive but professional approach.

Finally, thanks to our three children Alex, Rachel and Naomi who gave me a goal in the struggle to survive. This book is dedicated to them.

April 1994

Roy Hayim